MW00651702

Diets Don't Work®
The Structured Program

Healing the Cycles of Yo-Yo Dieting and Emotional Overeating

Rebecca Cooper

ReBu Publishing
Orange County, California
USA

This book is intended as a general guide to the topics discussed. It is not intended and should not be used as a substitute for professional help.

Diets Don't Work®-is a registered trademark, owned by Rebecca Cooper.

Published by:
ReBu Publishing
23861 El Toro Road, 7th Floor
Lake Forest, CA 92630

Copyright © 1999, 2009 by Rebecca Cooper

All rights reserved. This book may not be reproduced or transmitted in any form or by any means without written permission of the author. Chapter Exercises may be photocopied with the header and footer in place.

Cover Design: Sheridan O'Brien, www.SheridanDesignGroup.com
Copy Editor: Rhonda Seamonds, www.WriteReflections.com
Proofreading: Cynthia Lerner, www.ColoradoProof.com

Printed and Bound: Thomson-Shore Inc.

Printed in the United States of America

ISBN-13: 978-0-9728883-0-1
ISBN-10: 0-9728883-0-6

Diet's Don't Work®

Table of Contents

Acknowledgments... i

INTRODUCTION *You Are Courageous* v

My Journey viii

CHAPTER 1 *Facing the Fact that Diets Don't Work* 17

The Solution... 20

Coming Home to Our Appetite 21

What I Need to Take Care of Me 23

A Funny Thing about Metabolism 24

Janet and Stephanie's Progress 24

A Program that Works 25

Why do I do what I do?... 26

CHAPTER EXERCISE: Timeline.................................. 29

CHAPTER 2 *Where We Are Now* 31

Definition of Emotional Eating.................................... 34

The Food Coping Cycle 36

Getting Out of the Cycle 38

CHAPTER EXERCISE: Examine the Binge Cycle 41

CHAPTER 3 *Coming Home to You* 43

Our Most Important Relationship 44

Please Hear What I'm Not Saying [1] 45

The Different Parts of the Self..47

Healing the Separation 48

Physical 48

Emotional 49

Mental...50

Spiritual 50

Summary for Healing the Separation 51

Balance 52

CHAPTER EXERCISE: My Hunger Rating................................55

CHAPTER EXERCISE: Food Effects................................. 56

CHAPTER 4 *Stuffing Your Feelings* 59

What Are Feelings? 59

Stuffing Our Feelings 60

Common Defenses against Feelings..61

A Closer Look 62

Freedom from Our Defenses 64

Reacting Instead of Responding..66

Tools for Dealing with Feelings 69

CHAPTER EXERCISE: Actions for Feelings 71

CHAPTER 5 *Change Your Thinking, Change Your Life*... 73

Self-Talk 73

The Second Thought 74

Distorted Thinking 76

What Leads to a Changed Mindset 79

The Path Out of Disordered Eating 80

Obstacles to Growth and Joy 81

One Minute to Think 82

One Minute to Think 83

CHAPTER EXERCISE: Changing Self Talk 85

CHAPTER 6   *Exploring Your Beliefs & Values* 87

What Do You Believe? 87

Subconscious Beliefs 88

What Are My Spiritual Beliefs? 91

Being True to Me 94

Knowing Your Values 94

LIST OF VALUES 96

Summary 97

CHAPTER EXERCISE- Self Alignment 98

CHAPTER 7   *Boundaries* 101

The Building of Boundaries 102

Lack of Boundaries and Disordered Eating 103

Boundaries Create Honesty 104

Over-Committing 105

Setting Appropriate Boundaries 105

Overstepping Boundaries 106

My Experience..107

Carl Jung's Remarks..108

CHAPTER EXERCISE: Investigating Boundaries......... 110

CHAPTER 8   *Self-Discovery and Healing* 113

How to Know... 113

The Healing Power of Journaling...............................114

My Journaling Experience..115

The Journaling Process 116

Process 1: Automatic Writing.................................... 117

Process 2: Writing Yourself a Letter 118

Process 3: Write a letter to someone from the past or present
.... 119

CHAPTER EXERCISE: One Page Journaling................. 120

CHAPTER 9   *The Blessing of Self-Esteem* 121

Self-Esteem Explained 123

Self-Validation 124

Random Acts of Kindness.. 125

Esteemable Habits.. 126

Reinforcing Self-Esteem with Affirmations 127

Affirmations.. 128

10 Keys to Maintaining Healthy Self-Esteem........................... 130

Self-Esteem Test 131

CHAPTER EXERCISE- Installing Affirmations 132

CHAPTER 10 *Overcoming Emotional Eating* 135

A Vicious Cycle... 136

Ways to Reduce Stress.. 138

An Increased Need for Food as Fuel?..................................... 140

Additional Solutions 140

Changing Your Thinking 141

Relaxation 142

Strategies to Curb Emotional Eating....................................... 143

CHAPTER EXERCISE-Food Triggers 145

CHAPTER 11 *Coping in New Ways* 147

Loss of Control 148

Facing Our Feelings... 149

Anxiety.. 149

Benefiting from Anxiety 151

Some Facts about Anger and Eating..152

Tools for Dealing with Anger..153

Is it really Fear?...154

Is it really Hurt?..155

Other Considerations...155

Simple Ways to Quiet a Noisy Mind...156

Finding Happiness..157

CHAPTER EXERCISE- New Ways of Coping............................160

CHAPTER 12   *Filling the Emptiness* 163

A Call from Within...164

Dependence... 164

Spiritual Dependence..167

Researching Spirituality's Effects 167

CHAPTER EXERCISE -Expanding Your Spirituality..............169

CHAPTER 13 *Assertiveness Matters* 171

What Assertiveness Is and Isn't.. 172

Claim Your Assertive Rights..174

Becoming More Assertive...175

A Look at Assertive Communication 176

CHAPTER EXERCISE: Becoming More Assertive..................179

CHAPTER 14   *Forgiveness Frees Us* 181

What Is Forgiveness? 182

Underlying Feelings 182

Being "Triggered" 184

Changing Our Patterns 186

My Mother and Self-Forgiveness 188

The Power of Self-Forgiveness 189

CHAPTER EXERCISE-A Self-Forgiveness Letter 190

CHAPTER 15   *Living Diet Free!* 193

Natural Eating 193

Remembering the Goal 195

Breakfast – Don't Skip It! 197

CHAPTER EXERCISE: What I am Willing to Do 198

CHAPTER 16   *The Power of* 201

Purpose & Goals 201

Your Purpose Is Unique 202

Discovering Your Purpose 202

Finding Your Way 203

Job or Passion 205

Where Will You Spend Your Energy? 206

An Ongoing Story 207

CHAPTER EXERCISE: Part I. Finding Our Purpose 209

Resources 215

List of Figures.. 219

Index... 220

About the Author 223

Ordering Information.. 225

Acknowledgments

I have been gifted with the most amazing team who has helped me in my vision of creating a center to help people with disordered eating and eating disorders; I would like to express my deepest appreciation for my team at Diets Don't Work® and Rebecca's House Eating Disorder Treatment Programs™.

I have also been helped along my personal path by so many people. I would like to first thank my husband and my best friend, Coop, for sharing a wonderful life and true love with me; my loving sister, Rhonda Seamonds, who I love beyond measure; my high school math teacher, Ernestine Capehart and her family, who allowed me to be a part of their happy family; Ann Garrett; Lois Montgomery; Bobbi Nesheim; and all the other defining relationships that helped me become the person I am today.

Rebecca Cooper

Dedication

I wish to dedicate this book to the memory of my mother and all others who have not found the way out of disordered eating. May this book create a new awareness in you.

You Are Courageous

I woke up or came to. I felt tired and sick. I was suffering with a hangover because of the sugar coma I put myself into the night before. Why did I do that? I was just going to have a small cup of ice cream. Then I saw the remains of my sister's birthday cake. It registered slowly. I had restrained myself initially because I had been *good* all day, but then I thought *I'll have one little piece.* Then it all came back to me as I replayed the events in my mind.

The "Moose Tracks" ice cream was delicious. Maybe I would have just a little more. I went to the kitchen and refilled my cup with the scrumptious treat; again, I noticed the cake I had avoided all day. I went back to bed and continued watching the Discovery channel. After I finished, I put the now empty cup on the night-stand.

Then the dialogue started. *Well, I really blew it. I wonder how many fat grams and calories I consumed. I bet it was more than I had all day. What a waste! What a big waist I would have in the morning. I have no willpower. I am such a failure. I may as well eat the cake too.*

I walked back into the kitchen, got a plate, and put a large slice of cake on it. As I was turning off the kitchen light, I thought, *Ice cream would be good with the cake.* I placed a scoop of ice cream on the plate that matched the serving of cake. Of course, I needed a bite of ice cream to go with each bite of cake. What about a little chocolate syrup to go over the whole thing. Yummy! I climbed into bed with my fabulous dessert. I looked at the TV. I wasn't watching it anymore. I was not present. I was with my best friend - food. I fell asleep with the television blaring.

Today, I would stick to my diet. I skipped breakfast and went off to work. I had a salad for lunch and secretly commended myself for not having any bread. I was being *good*.

By the afternoon, I was so tired and sleepy that I couldn't even think. More coffee would help. I ended up working late, as is my habit. When I got home, I turned on the kitchen light and the last piece of cake called my name. And so it began again.

Most of my clients felt hopeless when they finally came to the conclusion that *diets just don't work*. I know this feeling because I've been there too. Even when we've been through it all, if a new diet hits the media, we think this one will be the diet that will work! Once more, we try to be *good* and follow the plan perfectly, that is until we slip and then slide back into the vortex of failed diets, emotional overeating, and hopelessness.

Over the years, I've researched diets extensively. I have talked with many clients who have struggled with one diet after the next. Together, we have found some common experiences. The truth is that all diets work...*temporarily.* The only problem is that eventually we go off the diet. Then the weight comes back with a vengeance. We find ourselves bingeing on all the forbidden foods. Perhaps we just start eating normally, but *still* gain weight. We may get sick easily because our eating habits have weakened our immune system. Sometimes we have even developed dependence on substances like laxatives and drugs to maintain our weight. Some of us have developed eating disorders or died in the pursuit of our *perceived* ideal weight. Most of us have been on the yo-yo dieting rollercoaster so long we don't know how to get off. But we all started with a diet, so you get my drift about not being a fan of diets.

Interestingly, most of my clients could write books about nutrition, dieting and exercise. *They have the knowledge. They just cannot put it into practice for lasting results.* Lifestyle changes, pills, drinks, exercise, healthy eating, wraps, surgery, abstinence, duct tape…you name it. You may know what works for you in the short-term, but the question is *how do you make it work for a lifetime?*

In my work, I have counseled people of many different sizes. I've seen that attaining the perfect size doesn't really free someone from the diet mentality. I have found the real issue to be the amount of time you spend <u>thinking</u> about food, weight, diet, or body size. You can be at the perfect weight and still be consumed with these thoughts. How often do you think about this? If you're currently on a diet, how much do you think about the next meal or what you will or will not eat?

How is your social life affected by your dietary restrictions? Maybe a better question is how much of a social life have you missed because of food, weight, or how you felt your body looked? Maybe you just avoided the event entirely because nothing in your closet fit, or you were too tired, or you were afraid the food served would not be on your diet.

Maybe you attended the event, but were you present? How much time were you allowing food or thoughts of food, weight, or body image to consume you? This thinking diverts us from being in the now, or being present. In your mind, are you always in weight competition with every person you see? Are you wondering if they are thinking whether you are fat or skinny? Do you see how this interferes with our relationships?

Here's a clarifying example. I can remember talking to a friend, all the while thinking about going to the fast food restaurant on the way home. She asked me, "Where are you?"

I guess I had that glazed over look that often accompanies the thoughts of an upcoming feast. I was not present. I was physically standing in front of her, but I was not there. Has this ever happened to you?

There's a better way than dieting and the cycle of returning to emotional bingeing. I invite you now to an exciting and life-shifting path of self-awareness, understanding, and healing. But first, a little about me and how I came to create this program.

My Journey

In order to gain the acceptance and love I wanted, I believed I needed to look *right*, so I started my first diet at age thirteen. It was successful until I slipped, and since I already had blown it, I unconsciously figured I might as well eat all the things I had been denying myself. I didn't make the connection that dieting eventually results in binges. Thus began the frantic attempts to keep my body weight in control. I tried every new diet and weight control method I could find. This sent me into a vortex of an eating disorder. I even traveled the extreme ends of the continuum of disordered eating. This consumed twenty years of my life.

My life focus was my weight, body size, and constant thoughts of what to eat or not to eat. The scale determined how I would feel for the day. It determined what activities I would engage in, or if I would isolate, with or without the food, that day. It's sad to admit that my life's meaning and purpose at that time was *to be thin*. What a waste of human potential!

I have been free from this merry-go-round of yo-yo dieting and emotional binge eating for many years. Today, I find this experience invaluable in my work of helping people to change their eating habits. I have successfully worked with thousands of clients battling the effects of yo-yo dieting, emotional eating, and eating disorders. Now I am actually grateful for my battle with food. It changed my life and the lives of many others for the good!

I am often amazed about how my life's work manifested. I left the corporate world and went back to school, become a therapist, certified eating disorder specialist, authored the Diets Don't Work® structured program, founded Rebecca's House Transitional Living for Eating Disorders, and started Rebecca's House Eating Disorders Treatment Programs™ in Southern California. Isn't it amazing how much energy we have when we replace our unhealthy eating patterns and food obsession with a life?

Thank you for having the courage to read my book. I invite you to read this book with an inner awareness. Pay attention to what your gut is telling you about the passage you just read. Does it line up with your experiences and truth? Do you even know what your inner wisdom is telling you? Most of us have disconnected from our appetite and feelings and our inner wisdom. We are so accustomed to using an external form of direction that we aren't even aware of our own truth anymore. I believe this is one of the core reasons for disordered eating. We have lost touch with our appetite, our internal guidance system, and ourselves. Because of not having this connection, we are so willing to follow someone else's direction, instead of our own truth. Within the following pages, you will find the way to reclaim your real Self and end dieting forever!

There are many assessments, forms, and checklists, that you can download at www.DietsDontWork.org. I recommend starting with http://DietsDontWork.org/assessment. It will help you assess your eating style. This can point you to the corresponding chapters, sessions, or guided imageries of the Diets Don't Work® structured program that will best help you.

Which Diets Have You Tried?

☐   Atkins Diet Plan

☐   Best Life Diet

☐   Biggest Loser Diet

☐   Blood Type Diet

☐   Body for Life

☐   Bread Diet

☐   Cabbage Soup Diet

☐   Cheater's Diet

☐   Cookie Diet

☐   Eat Right for Your Type

☐   Eat This, Not That

☐   Fast Food Diet

☐   Fat Smash Diet

☐   Flat Belly Diet

☐   5 Factor Diet

☐   Flavor Point Diet

☐   Fruit Flush Diet

☐   French Women Don't Get Fat

- ☐ Glycemic Index Diet

- ☐ Grapefruit Diet

- ☐ Hallelujah Diet

- ☐ LA Weight Loss

- ☐ Lemonade Diet

- ☐ Living Low-Carb

- ☐ Macrobiotic Diet

- ☐ Martha's Vineyard Diet Detox

- ☐ Mayo Clinic Diet

- ☐ Medifast Diet

- ☐ Mediterranean Diet

- ☐ Milk Diet

- ☐ Morning Banana Diet

- ☐ Negative Calorie Diet

- ☐ New Beverly Hills Diet

- ☐ NutriSystem Diet

- ☐ Omega Diet

- ☐ Ornish Diet

- ☐ Paleo Diet

☐   Park Avenue Diet

☐   Perricone Diet

☐   Personality Type Diet

☐   Pritikin Diet

☐   Protein Power

☐   Raw Foods Diet

☐   Rice Diet Solution

☐   Scarsdale Medical Diet

☐   Shangri-La Diet

☐   Skinny Vegan Diet

☐   Slim-Fast Plan

☐   Sonoma Diet

☐   South Beach Diet

☐   South Beach Diet Supercharged

☐   Spectrum Diet

☐   Step Diet

☐   Sugar Busters

☐   Thin for Life

☐   3 Day Diet

□   3-Hour Diet

□   Ultimate Weight Solution

□   UltraMetabolism Diet

□   Volumetrics

□   Watermelon Diet

□   Weight Loss Cure

□   Weight Watchers

□   You – On a Diet

□   Zone Diet

What diet worked for you? Do you see my point?

All diets work

… temporarily.

CHAPTER 1   # *Facing the Fact that Diets Don't Work*

Have you ever dieted and gained the weight back?
What really works?
This book offers ideas that will serve you for a lifetime.

Have you ever been on a diet before? More than once? Many times? Did you gain the weight back after going off the diets? Think to yourself about how many times you have tried this before...then ask yourself, *does dieting really work?*

STATISTICS show that sixty-six percent of America's population is overweight. Nearly *one-third* are obese.[1] Most are eating low-fat, low-calorie, and diet foods. There are more

---

[1] US Dept of Health and Mental Services.

overweight people in the United States today than any time in history!

At the same time, Americans are spending over $60 billion on dieting and weight-loss products each year, and this does not take into account the rising numbers of gastric bypass surgeries being performed[2]. Weight loss has become *a national obsession.* Something is drastically wrong!

At any given point, 25 million Americans are seriously dieting and 40% to 60% are high school girls. Now, we have 42% of first to third grade children reporting they want to be thinner.[3] Only one out of every 200 dieters lose their weight and keep it off for a year or more. *Dieting is not working!*

35% of "normal dieters" progress to eating disorders.

Studies show that 35% of *normal dieters* progress to eating disorders.[4] Currently 8 million people in America have an eating disorder; 86% started by age 20.[5] Meanwhile, Anorexia Nervosa – an eating disorder in which patients starve themselves to continually lower their body weight – has the highest mortality rate of any mental diagnosis.

For some, gastric bypass surgery has become the only option. Many people find that the surgery does not work or they develop secondary addictions. Thirty percent of post-bariatric or gastric bypass surgery patients develop a substance addiction.[6] The body may change, but the thinking remains the same. Left untreated, many bariatric clients gain back their weight. Now what?

At least 50,000 individuals will die each year as a direct result of their eating disorder. Because of the secretiveness, shame, and under-diagnosis associated with these disorders, many cases are not reported. Also, many deaths are attributed

---

2"The U.S. Weight Loss & Diet Control Market."
3 Collins, M.E. (1991). Body figure perceptions and preferences among preadolescent children. International Journal of Eating Disorders, 199-208.
4 Shisslak, C.M., Crago, M., & Estes, L.S. (1995). The Spectrum of Eating Disturbances. International Journal of Eating Disorders, 18 (3): 209-219.
5 National Association of Anorexia Nervosa and Associated Disorders; 2006
6 Moorehead, M., Alexander, C.L., (2007). Transfer of Addictions & Consideration for Preventive Measures in Bariatric Surgery, Bariatric Times.

to other causes when the underlying problems are obesity and/or malnutrition. **There has to be a different way to approach healthy eating!**

In my practice, I have learned how clients of *all* sizes are haunted with disordered eating. The lady that sat in front of me may be meticulously dressed, looking like she just stepped from the cover of a magazine, but I wanted to cry when she talked about what she was doing to maintain this image. I knew her torment. She told me of a life limited by yo-yo dieting, uncontrollable thoughts of food, weight, and body image, and a total disconnection with her Self. She told me of a life lived behind a mask, the only life she now knew.

Clients of all sizes are haunted with disordered eating.

Then there was the mother that came to see me because she loved her small children so much. She was distraught because she would get angry with them when they wanted her attention and she needed to eat. She worried about the example she was setting for her daughters. She talked of her estrangement from her loving husband. She hated her body and the person she had become. She used food to soothe herself and to calm herself, and it was the only thing she looked forward to in the evenings when the kids were finally in bed. She knew this was not the life she wanted to live, but saw no way out.

A client came to me because she needed heart surgery. The surgeons were afraid to operate on her because of her weight. She went on a medically supervised liquid diet to lose the weight. She cried to me that she wanted to live. She wanted to participate in her grandchildren's lives, but she told me she was going to a fast food restaurant on the way home from the hospital. She said she would have her liquid diet drink and follow it up with eating enough for three people. She just couldn't stop and didn't understand why.

My clients came because they inherently knew that there had to be a different answer other than the dieting. It just had not worked for them. I was reminded that a definition for insanity is doing the same thing over and over again and expecting different results. Together, we found a way out of the insanity. My book will share our collective experience and wisdom. There is hope, and you can do this!

The Solution

So what's the solution to this problem? I have found that the reason diets don't work long-term is because a diet is an external form of control. We eat what is on our food plan in the proper amount, at the appropriate time, and prepared the specific way. It does nothing to clue us into what we are experiencing in our body, except maybe if we experience hunger - real hunger. What do we do with that awareness? We stuff it down and feel good that we stuck to our diet, or maybe we cheat and eat all the forbidden foods. Once more, we suffer the consequences of slipping off our diet. We beat ourselves up for not obeying the food plan. We once more reinforce the idea that it's not okay to pay attention to our body's signals. Something else, the diet, is supposed to know what we need. The problem is that with dieting, we disconnect from our internal appetite and Self.

One of my favorite clients came to see me, so happy about eating packaged frozen diet meals all week. My response was, "Isn't it amazing that that company knew exactly what you needed? They knew you were a 200 pound man, your height, with your activity level. The thing I can't figure out is how they knew to package it for you, instead of the 130 pound woman who bought the same package." Although we both had a good laugh, how many people are doing this?

I have found that external controls around food work only temporarily. Then we rebel.

I have found that external controls around food work only temporarily. Then we rebel. It seems that we're not programmed to follow someone else's food plan or diet, at least not indefinitely. We always rebel against the diet – sometimes quickly and sometimes we can last a long time. Eventually, however, the scale starts to climb.

Plus, each day as we weigh ourselves, we think that what we see on the scale will make a tremendous difference in our lives. It does, but only because it's like a horoscope, coloring our mood for the day.

I have seen amazing results when people can internalize new eating behaviors. They are in touch with their body's signals and being *true to themselves*. Their healthy metabolism is restored. They lose weight as a by-product of this new way of living. This works! My book is designed to help you find ways of changing your eating patterns from the inside out.

Coming Home to Our Appetite

Yes, we need to work *from the inside out*. This shift changes the way we relate to food and to ourselves. We reconnect with our own innate abilities, eating when hungry and stopping when full. *Our bodies were created to function in this manner.*

In time, with practice, our powerful internal skills will become stronger and we will begin to feel our natural appetite. We learn to follow our internal clues. These skills can be summed up by the phrase *being true to ourselves*.

Essentially, we come back home to ourselves. We honor our body's signals of physical hunger. We become aware of the connection between how we feed our physical body and how we feel. We can rate our fullness or sense of being satiated, and determine where we are and where we would like to be. If we are hungry, but know we are going to a fabulous dinner in an hour, we may decide to have an apple because we are paying attention to our appetite, but still want to be hungry for that dinner. We can *have our cake and eat it too*!

We also honor our body's need to be active and to feel strong. We see that regular exercise raises our metabolism and makes us feel good. We have a sense of well-being. We get connected to our physical body. We see our muscles becoming stronger, and become more confident in our abilities.

In addition, *a large part of personal growth is that we learn to honor our feelings and come to understand that food does not work for emotional reasons*. By acknowledging a feeling, we

We learn to honor our feelings, and come to understand that food does not work for emotional reasons.

don't have to use food or obsess about our weight to push it from our awareness. Once we are aware, we can actually substitute an *effective way of helping ourselves.* Food does not fix feelings. The focus on food, weight, and diets temporarily numbs our feelings. They then resurface again – and again – and again. By learning what we need, we can take care of ourselves. We learn balance. Balance comes when we are connected to the core of ourselves. In this state of balance, we naturally eat when we are hungry, make healthy choices, and stop when we are full.

By taking responsibility for ourselves, we give ourselves choices. We can give ourselves all the love, compassion, time, etc. that we need. When we choose to take time for ourselves, we have that energy and love to give to others. You can't give what you don't have – that is, a resource of energy and love that only comes from self-care and self-love. As an added benefit, those around you will perceive your positive modeling and maybe even catch on to the idea of nurturing themselves.

As we experience a shift from the external controls to our True Self, we get in touch with a method of eating that we forgot long ago. To start exploring yourself now, consider the following questions throughout the day.

1. Am I physically hungry?

How do I experience hunger? On a scale of 1 to 10 – with 10 being stuffed and 1 being starved – where am I? Where do I want to be? What will get me there? When did I last eat? What is my body asking for really?

2. How do I feel?

Ask yourself, am I physically hungry or do I have a feeling or thought that I want to go away? Check for feelings and sensations. Recognize what it feels like to be grateful, happy, secure, proud, loved, rested, satisfied, or healthy. Do I use food when I am bored, angry, sad, afraid, guilty, lonely, hungry, tired, sick, etc.?

3. What do I need?

Once you know how you feel, you can move your attention from your heart to your mind and logically find the corresponding need. Example are if you feel tired, you need to rest for a few minutes; if you are sleepy, sleep or meditate; if you are lonely, call a friend; if you are angry, write about it, talk to a friend, or find another way to express your feelings other than using food. Do you have a body part in pain that needs attention?

4. Do I need support?

Many of us have gone to food for comfort and support. Do you have a support system? Who can you go to when you are in need? Where do you get your needs met? It's important that we don't let a sense of false pride hold us back from getting our needs met. Isolation is a downfall for many of us!

5. What am I saying to myself?

Listen to yourself-talk. Would you speak to your friend like you do to yourself? (For most of us as we are facing our inner healing, the answer is *definitely not!)* Is yourself-talk supporting your goals?

What I Need to Take Care of Me

We need to access where we are right now. Check the items below that would help you take better care of yourself.

- ☐ Adequate nutrition
- ☐ A connection with my body, mind, and spirit
- ☐ A healthy rested body
- ☐ Intellectual stimulation
- ☐ A positive attitude
- ☐ The ability to know and speak my truth
- ☐ A healthy spirituality that provides support and comfort
- ☐ Emotional intimacy with healthy individuals
- ☐ Physical assistance from other people
- ☐ A sense of community, family, and support

My book will help you begin taking better care of your needs, starting today!

A Funny Thing about Metabolism

There's something else that's important for you to consider when it comes to why diets don't work.

Diets slow your metabolism.

Many dieters skip meals and consume a low amount of calories in order to achieve their weight loss goals. What they don't realize is that the body has a built-in mechanism that will fight against you when you use these tactics. That mechanism is called *metabolism*. Simply put, your metabolism is the rate at which your body burns calories. Restrictive, low calorie diets slow your metabolism.

Our metabolism evolved in this way to protect us from starvation. Severely restricting calories and skipping meals puts the body in *starvation mode*. What the body is trying to do is to make the most of the food calories that you have ingested. This makes it difficult to lose weight. Our body works against our efforts. It will hold onto every last morsel because it doesn't trust it will be full again. It is self-preservation.

We see this phenomenon at my clinic every day. Let's look at how two women did – the first on the program described in this book and the second a woman who was skipping meals.

Janet and Stephanie's Progress

Janet was eating three meals a day based on the demands of her natural appetite. She was exercising two to three times per week for twenty to sixty minutes at a time. She lost two pounds in two weeks. Then our exercise physiologist repeated her body fat composition and metabolic rate tests. The tests revealed she had actually lost three pounds of fat, but gained one pound of muscle. Her metabolic rate had increased. If she ate the same amount she had eaten previously, she would lose more weight because of her new metabolic rate and muscle mass.

During the same time, her friend, Stephanie, skipped breakfast and ate a small salad in the afternoon. She usually had a *normal* dinner with a few snacks later at night, which was usually something simple like a low-fat yogurt or cereal. Stephanie did not exercise, but she also lost two pounds. However, when her body fat composition and metabolic rates were calculated, she had actually lost one pound of fat and one pound of muscle. Her metabolic rate had decreased because of the loss of lean body mass or muscle. If she continued to eat the same in the next month, she would gain weight due to her decreased metabolism.

It's important to note that the amount of food eaten was not the only factor at play in this example. Exercise was the other crucial issue. In addition to food intake, metabolism is also affected by the amount of muscle that we carry on our bodies. Janet's approach allowed her to build muscle, which will support her goals over the long-term. Meanwhile, Stephanie is actually lowering her metabolism because of her weight loss strategies – a killer combination of erratic eating and lack of exercise. Her body was forced to use muscle as fuel because Stephanie just wasn't consuming enough.

Let's look ahead a little. Because of her restrictive approach, Stephanie is also more likely to go off her program sooner. That's when she'll really pay the price for lowering her metabolism. Even if Stephanie eats a healthy amount of calories, her body will burn fewer calories because her metabolism decreased. As a result, she will continue to gain weight.

With all the stress she's putting on her body and Self, Stephanie is also more vulnerable to going off her diet and plunging into emotional overeating. We'll take a look at that issue in the next chapter.

A Program that Works

Today we have more fat-free, low-fat, no-carbohydrate, low-in-calorie, light, and diet foods available than any time in history! Every magazine we pick up has the newest weight loss solution. The available diet books could fill an entire library. There are weight loss clinics offering a wide assortment of every fad diet you could imagine.

If all these diets worked, 70 percent of Americans would not *still* be on a diet. We would not be seeing the 36 percent increase in obesity that we've had over the last ten years.[5] Ninety-five percent of dieters *would not* be regaining their weight, plus more, with each failure!

As I was explaining earlier, every traditional weight loss program sets limits and gives people a false sense of control. Sometimes, the most strict or bizarre diets seem to work best because they give the most precise instructions and, therefore, the strongest sense of control. We can feel in control as long as we do exactly as the program or diet outlines, but what happens when we make a mistake? Don't we fall into patterns that sabotage us and lead to weight gain?

Every time I went on a diet, I would be hopeful and enthusiastic. I would tell all my friends about this new diet plan, and it was working! I felt so good about my new resolve. As I lost weight, I would get compliments about my efforts. Sometimes, I even bought *skinny* clothes. I was on a high!

Then, after awhile, I ate something that I was not *supposed* to eat. My friends asked about my diet. I didn't tell them I cheated because I wasn't going to cheat again, but I always did. I noticed I was becoming more irritable, anxious, and depressed. I felt overwhelmed and forgot things easily. Then I would find myself having just a bite of my favorite binge food, then another. Now I didn't want to see my friends. They had seen me on this rollercoaster so many times before. I hated myself. Why was I doing this?

Why do I do what I do?

In view of all this, the crucial points to remember about why diets don't work are these:

For a program to succeed long-term, it must create an internal change.

- Following other people's food plans and going on diet after diet have disconnected us from ourselves and our appetites.
- After a while, we get *fed up* with listening to everyone but ourselves. We rebel.
- In our rebellion, we eat all of the foods we have been denying ourselves, and the weight comes back on.

- We must deal with the underlying internal issues or we stay on the yo-yo diet rollercoaster.

Traditional weight loss programs all rely on an external source of control and *limit setting*. The real solution to weight problems requires far more than external controls. By now, it may well be intuitively clear to you that for a program to succeed long-term, it must create an internal change.

That internal change is exactly what *Diets Don't Work*® is about. By reading this book, you will learn:

1. How to connect with your True Self.

2. How to identify what triggers your emotional overeating.

3. How to recognize the *need* to overeat.

4. How to recognize your feelings and walk through them.

5. How to calm and center yourself without using emotional overeating.

6. How to deal with the mental obsession of food, diet, and body image.

7. How to become your own best friend and treat yourself as you would treat any other friend that you care for.

8. How to improve other relationships in your lives. (When we love ourselves, we can love others more fully.)

9. How to take action with the help of your subconscious and automatically use new coping mechanisms in your daily life.

10. How to let go of the emotional conflicts that you have pushed down with food or shoved out of mind with a dieting obsession.

11. How to see a new way of viewing nutrition and exercise in your life and how to incorporate this self-care on a subconscious level.

12. How to recognize if food allergies or nutritional cravings are interfering with your ability to develop healthy eating patterns.

13. How to handle some of life's most challenging moments, including times of grief and loss, without returning to destructive habits.

14. How to move on with a new meaning and purpose in life.

15. How we need to replace the time and energy we have spent on food with our passions. As we are getting in touch with our Self, we will come to know our passions.

As you'll soon see first-hand, *Diets Don't Work*® is much more than an approach to eating and weight loss. It is an approach to life! It's about dealing with your life and all the things that are currently making you turn to eating or an obsessive focus on diet and body image. It's about you learning to love and take care of you.

When you get down to it, that's really what you've been trying to accomplish with dieting and compulsive overeating all along.

In the next chapter, we'll take a look at the emotional overeating cycle that develops when a diet starts to fail. But first, let's access where you are now.

How did your disordered eating begin? Many clients have found awareness with the Timeline Exercise on the next page. Complete the significant events timeline first and then continue to the relationships line. Line up the events according to timeframes. Use these dates to position the remaining events on the following timelines. Put a star next to any weight gain or loss that was artificially induced.

Don't forget to download the following:
http://DietsDontWork.org/assessment
http://DietsDontWork.org/forms/checklist
http://DietsDontWork.org/forms/calendar

CHAPTER EXERCISE: Timeline

Birth

<u>Today</u>

Significant Events
List 8-10 events in
your life (relocation,
illnesses, life changes, etc)

Relationships
(i.e., marriages,
deaths, etc.)

Spiritual
(i.e., religious events,
awarenesses, etc)

Weight
Above ideal weight
Ideal weight
Below ideal weight

© 1998 Rebecca Cooper

www.dietsdontwork.org

800-711-6336

CHAPTER 2

Where We Are Now

Our food associations influence us

and foster the habit of turning to food for emotional relief.

I just cannot stop eating ice cream. Mary was distraught over her weight gain and inability to stop eating ice cream. We started talking about her early associations with the sweet treat. She recalled an event that occurred many times in her childhood. She was the youngest of three children. She remembered going to a Dairy Queen frequently with her mother. I asked, "Was this an unhappy time for you as a child?" She said it was not. Her father was away a lot. Her mother was upset about her fathers' absence. The Dairy Queen was across the street from the bar that her father frequented. When her mother became anxious because Dad was not home, she would take Mary to the Dairy Queen to see if Dad's car was in the bar parking lot. She would wait outside in the car, eating her ice cream until Mom could find out who Dad was with. Mom was always crying on the way home, but Mary just immersed herself in her frozen treat. It hurt to see Mom so upset. She didn't understand why they always went to get ice cream and Mom was always crying and crying. She just couldn't understand then what she knows now. Mary suddenly understood why she felt the uncontrollable urge for the frozen treat whenever she was anxious or confused. These emotions were hardwired to ice cream. It made sense to her. Now, when she had an uncontrollable desire for ice cream, she got in touch with that feeling. Eventually, Mary was able to link more self-soothing behaviors with this feeling, and formed a new habit of really taking care of her little girl.

We develop patterns of behavior early in life. We start associating certain behaviors with certain events. For example, being fed by our parents when we were young may have represented being cared for or being loved. On the other hand, not being fed when we were hungry may have caused us to wonder if there would be enough food in the future. Maybe we should eat it all right now.

Food may also serve as a distraction. For instance, as children, we may have been told at the doctor's office that if we don't cry when we get a shot, we will get a lollipop. Therefore, we focused on getting the lollipop instead of feeling the fear or pain of the needle. We effectively blocked the pain and focused on the reward – the sugar. Is it any wonder that later in life when we experience pain – emotional or physical – that we think a candy bar will make us feel better?

We may associate happy occasions, holidays and celebrations, with food. We remember the togetherness, love, and joy of these special events. As a result, we look to food to recapture the feelings of those joyful events with our childhood holiday foods.

We may learn that we can have dessert if we are good. Thus, dessert becomes a reward, an acknowledgement of success. We trudge through a hard day at work, knowing a reward awaits us at the end of the day.

When we were young, we may have been instructed to eat everything on our plate. We were coached not to pay attention to our appetite. Some of us have never gotten in touch with this internal cue. We don't know when we're hungry, what we're hungry for, and when we're full. We know what we should or should not eat, but we have learned this is not enough.

Some of us use food to get through the mundane, boring tasks of daily life. Food serves as a positive reinforcement to keep us from performing something that we would rather not do.

We can also use food to procrastinate, to avoid some action or responsibility that needs to be taken care of. We rationalize that it is okay to eat right now, even if we aren't physically hungry. We figure that we'll get to the task after we eat. Sometimes we find ourselves eating even more to put off the task a little longer.

We may be using food to cope with the stress in our lives. Over time, our destructive eating behavior actually makes the stress worse. We have less time and less energy.

We may feel like we have an empty hole inside of us, and we try to use food to make ourselves feel whole and complete. However, because we are automatically using food, we cannot discover what's truly disturbing us and what we really need.

We pick up so many associations between food and behavior in the course of our lives. Some are life-enhancing and some interfere with living well. Our food associations influence us and foster the habit of turning to food for emotional relief. We may not even be conscious of most of these associations. Nevertheless, they can and do influence us.

A first step in changing behavior is awareness. You can't change something if you're not even aware of it. Your associations with food and what it means to you will become more apparent through the work in this book. Here is a diagram that may explain this.

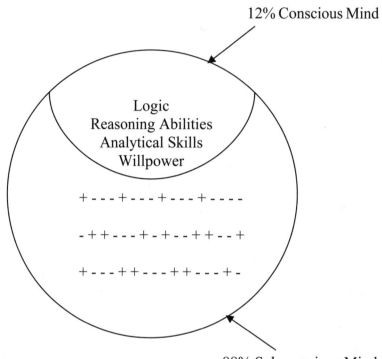

Figure 2.1: The Conscious and Subconscious Mind

Now let's look at what we do with these associations.

Definition of Emotional Eating

There's a difference between unhealthy eating habits and emotional eating. Some of us are consistently making unhealthy food choices. Our daily diet may consist of fried, sugary, or fast foods. (This is not to be confused with occasional unhealthy food choices.)

A person with an emotional eating issue is using food to cope with life. As compulsive overeaters, we overeat as a means to stuff down feelings or thoughts. We may use food to avoid some part of our lives. Many of the pleasant associations we have made with food over our lifetime now play into our choosing this method to soothe ourselves.

Emotional eating wears many different faces; we may graze or eat small amounts of food all day long, or we may eat large amounts in a short amount of time. Sometimes a tragedy, transition, or life change happens and we find ourselves turning to food to get through it. We may plan our binge knowing that when the family goes to bed, we will have our reprieve with the food. This emotional overeating is also known as binge eating.

Emotional overeating often starts in response to a diet. We restrict ourselves with a diet until we rebel and overeat. Sometimes we have been on a diet and slipped. Then we eat everything we have been denying ourselves.

Emotional eating also involves a mental obsession about food, weight, diet, or body image. It affects our self-esteem and robs us of the quality of life that we deserve. We may become depressed or anxious because of our eating patterns.

As an emotional eater, you've become hard-wired to eat when an unwanted feeling comes up.

It's important to realize that you've done the best you could up to this point. Don't beat yourself up for your previous actions. Remember that you were not aware of the underlying causes of your emotional eating. We need to identify why we are turning to food. We can easily do this by recognizing that food has become our best friend and a source of comfort.

It also helps to recognize that there is a relationship between our emotions and our eating behaviors. Emotional eating is just a symptom of the problem, rather than what is actually causing the problem. It is easy to focus on our weight or eating behaviors as the only problem. This prevents us from going in deeper to find the real root cause of our behavior.

All you need to start recovering is the willingness to change, to open your mind to a different type of approach.

Through this book, you'll learn about your individual triggers that set off the emotional overeating. You need to be aware of these triggers in order to change the behavior so you can achieve your goal. Various chapter exercises have been designed to help you change these behaviors, including the exercise at the end of Chapter 10. That chapter also provides more background on emotional eating.

Know now that our thoughts are the first link to our actions. If you reach out your hand, your mind has to tell your arm to move. We can identify the thoughts that are producing the unwanted act of eating when we are not physically hungry. These thoughts often stem from unconscious beliefs. We'll later explore these beliefs in Chapter 6.

The Food Coping Cycle

We can't do anything about the fact that things in life are going to throw us off balance. Life happens. We can't control everything that takes place in our environment. At this point, you may still feel the need to eat when such things upset you.

Upon entering the food coping cycle, you successfully manage to block out the original feelings with thoughts of food. The problem with this process is that the feelings get stuffed down over and over again. You don't get a chance to exercise other methods of coping, and soon food becomes your major coping mechanism. You become hard-wired to eat when an unwanted feeling comes up.

Let's take a closer look at this cycle to see what areas you identify with.

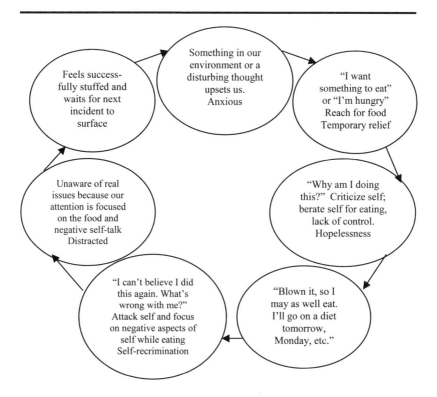

Figure 2.2: Food Coping Cycle

In the past, you may have focused on *just say no*. We know this doesn't work. We need to break the cycle at a different point, at the SELF TALK. You can break a cycle at any point – and the cycle does break. The area we want to focus on now is how we talk and treat ourselves today. This is an important first step in breaking the cycle.

"Just say no" does not work.

From examining our past habits, we have learned that repetition works. Starting with small steps and using repetition, we can now form new habits.

The food coping cycle has become a substitute for dealing effectively with other areas of our lives. We are using food to deal with our anxious thoughts and feelings. Remember, you have been doing the best you can up until now. You cannot change something of which you are not aware. The reaching for the food when we are not physically hungry is our red flag. It tells us that there is something going on that we need to pay attention to in that moment.

Change takes place in the present.

Change takes place in the present. We can't change what we ate in the past or what we will eat in the future. We begin change right now, with this meal, this bite.

We can work with ourselves instead of against ourselves. This is more like surrender. Don't demand it – just let it unfold. The body was designed to work in conjunction with our appetite by eating when we are hungry and stopping when we are full.

We need to get back in touch with this innate ability. Previous attempts at controlling food haven't worked so far, so let's take a different approach.

Freedom is thinking about food only when you are hungry or preparing for a meal.

Getting Out of the Cycle

Self-talk is self-hypnosis. Listen to what you are telling yourself on a daily basis.

Now that we have looked at the food coping cycle and discussed how the negative self-talk can affect our eating habits, how do we jump off this merry-go-round and train our thoughts to positively influence our lives?

The plan is to GIVE YOURSELF A BREAK. We have spent too much energy negatively criticizing ourselves in the past. Why is it we fail to acknowledge the many good things we accomplish in a day? This lopsided way of thinking can cause us to remain on that proverbial merry-go-round. It's time to start congratulating yourself for the things well done!

At first, you may want to start out with something simple. After making your bed in the morning, tell yourself, *I almost always accomplish making my bed!* or *nice job cleaning up the living room*, and progress to something larger. *Wow, good job handling that tough conversation with my co-worker.* Whatever the task, the point is that you can take moments throughout the day to congratulate yourself for the things you do well.

We need to break the cycle of negative self-talk, so start small if you need to. We want to get our attention off all the negative messages we are telling ourselves. In time, these repetitive affirming messages will begin a new cycle of behavior. Remember, repetition works. What you affirm, you create. Watch what you say about yourself to others as well. Is it something that you want to reinforce within yourself?

This practice of nurturing or re-parenting yourself will help you to become more attuned to your internal dialogue. It will also help you work on preventing yourself-talk from being a negative influence in your life.

Our intention is to learn to live our lives with confidence and self-acceptance. The negative self-talk accomplishes the exact opposite of this goal.

We cannot change something we are not even aware of.

As a beginning, we are looking to break the food coping cycle with better self-talk. There's more information on how to do this in Chapter 5, "Change Your Thinking, Change Your Life," and also in other sections in the book. The following exercise is a step toward awareness. We cannot change something of which we are not even aware.

DietsDon'tWork®

CHAPTER EXERCISE: Examine the Binge Cycle

Use this chart when you want to eat and you know you are not physically hungry, when you are constantly <u>thinking</u> about food, weight or body image, or when you suddenly become anxious, irritable, or depressed.

TIME?	WHERE WAS I?	WHO WAS I WITH?	WHAT WAS I FEELING?	WHAT DID I TELL MYSELF?	MY NOTES AFTER USING THE FOOD OR NOT EATING?

© 1999 Rebecca Cooper   www.dietsdontwork.org   800-711-6336

CHAPTER 3　　***Coming Home to You***

What is this self inside us,

This silent observer,

Severe and speechless critic,

Who can terrorize us

And urge us to futile activity,

And in the end,

Judge us still more severely

For the errors

Into which his own

Reproaches drove us?"

T.S. Eliot

When my clients come to my clinic, one of the hardest things they find to do is to do nothing. You may find that is when the urge to eat is the most intense. You may feel anxious, bored, or lonely. When you have nothing to do for a period of time, you are alone with your Self. Are you comfortable with that person? What kind of self-talk do you hear? Are there a lot of negative messages? How do you spend your time when you are your only company? Some will find many ways of distracting ourselves, filling up the space with noise, busyness, TV, drink, food, or even bad company. For some of us, any company is better than the one we have in our head.

Can you imagine how becoming your own best friend can change your world?

With the obsessive thoughts about food, diet, and weight, you disconnect from the pain of your emotions. More importantly, you also disconnect from your Self.

Now is the time to come home to you.

Our Most Important Relationship

Some of us are not aware of the importance of the relationship we have with our Self. We focus on our relationships with our mate, our friends, family, and co-workers, but we don't even recognize the necessity of a relationship with *numero uno* – that primary person in our lives, our Self!

Let's take a look at this for a moment. Our relationship with our Self starts at birth. When we are very young, we learn certain actions and reactions. We learn there are some behaviors that are more acceptable than others. We learn this best from the expressed approval or disapproval of the important <u>big</u> adults in our lives.

Our goal at this tiny age is to be loved. We just want to be accepted. We may find that it is not acceptable to be angry or sad or to speak our feelings. What do we do with these emotions? *Many of us disconnect from our true feelings and put on the appropriate mask so we will be loved and accepted.*

Food and the thoughts of food, weight, diet, and body image, separate us from Self, God, and others.

Over time, we may be so disconnected from our True Self that we don't even know what we are feeling. We may smile when we are sad or angry, and stop our thoughts before they leave our mouths. We may not even know our truth anymore. We bury all this behind a mountain of food, so we never become aware of what is really *eating* at us.

There are many ways that this disconnection is harmful in our lives. For example, because of it we may not know when to eat. As a result of dieting, we have disregarded our internal system of knowing when we are hungry and when we are full. We let some outside source (the diet) determine when we should eat or not eat, what to eat, and how much. We are born with the ability to know when we are hungry or full. We have just disconnected from our

Self and this natural ability. We need to reconnect to this important part of ourselves.

We come into this world and we leave this world with only one being – our Self. If we don't have this connection, life can be very hard and lonely. No other person or substance can provide us with what our internal Self can. Others may seem to fix it temporarily but, after a while, we are left alone again. If we don't have our Self, we are really alone.

It is a worthwhile endeavor to make the long journey back home to your Self. Your own Self can be your best friend. Can you imagine how becoming your own best friend can change your world? The bonus is that when you have gone this far, you can then connect to others because you are showing them who you really are. You are being true to your Self.

And there's more. Some people even say connecting with your Self connects you to your spirituality and you then can have a personal relationship with a *God of your understanding*. Others see this as connecting with your higher consciousness, universal goodness, or inherent internal wisdom.

You can always go back to the way you were. You know how to do that. Why not travel this journey home to Self to see how it makes a difference in your life? Read the following and see what comes up for you.

Please Hear What I'm Not Saying [1]

Don't be fooled by me.
Don't be fooled by the face I wear
for I wear a mask, a thousand masks,
masks that I'm afraid to take off,
and none of them is me.

Pretending is an art that's second nature with me,
but don't be fooled,
for God's sake don't be fooled.
I give you the impression that I'm secure,

"I wear a thousand masks, masks that I'm afraid to take off, and none of them are me."

that all is sunny and unruffled with me,
within as well as without,
that confidence is my name and coolness my game,
that the water's calm and I'm in command,
and that I need no one, but don't believe me.

My surface may seem smooth but my surface is my
mask, ever-varying and ever-concealing.
Beneath lies no complacence.
Beneath lies confusion, and fear, and aloneness.

Sometimes we create the "bondage of self" by the "masks we wear."

But I hide this. I don't want anybody to know it.
I panic at the thought of my weakness exposed.
That's why I frantically create a mask to hide behind,
a nonchalant sophisticated facade, to help me pretend,
to shield me from the glance that knows.

But such a glance is precisely my salvation,
my only hope, and I know it.
That is, if it's followed by acceptance,
if it's followed by love.

It's the only thing that can liberate me from myself,
from my own self-built prison walls,
from the barriers I so painstakingly erect.
It's the only thing that will assure me
of what I can't assure myself,
that I'm really worth something.

But I don't tell you this. I don't dare to, I'm afraid to.
I'm afraid your glance will not be followed by acceptance, will not be followed by love.
I'm afraid you'll think less of me,
that you'll laugh, and your laugh would kill me.
I'm afraid that deep-down I'm nothing
and that you will see this and reject me.

So I play my game, my desperate pretending game,
with a facade of assurance without

and a trembling child within.
So begins the glittering but empty parade of masks,
and my life becomes a front.

Go to http://www.poetrybycharlescfinn.com to read the ending of this thought provoking poem.

"Please Hear What I Am Not Saying" was given out to students, family, and friends by Charlie Finn when he was a beginning high school teacher in Chicago in 1966. From there, it has reappeared in multiple books, recordings, and websites around the world-- passed from hand to hand by people touched by its message. I was given this by one of the girls I was trying to help in the 80s. The story of how this has circulated the world can also be found at http://www.poetrybycharlesfinn.com.

The Different Parts of the Self

We are made up of a physical, emotional, mental, and spiritual Self. *Each part needs nourishment.* What if we are trying to fill our emotional emptiness with food? What if we need spiritual food and we use physical food? The empty part of us will never get satisfied or filled. Some of us feel that we have an empty hole inside that food just cannot fill. No matter how much food we eat, it doesn't satisfy that internal hunger.

How do we know what part of our Self needs something, especially if we have used food and our emotional overeating for every need in the past? How do we know if it is physical or spiritual hunger? Our physical body needs food to survive. The emotional side of us needs emotional fulfillment. Our mental abilities need to be stimulated. The spiritual side of us needs spiritual energy and connection.

Here are some questions to get you started.

Physical Hunger

What does physical hunger feel like for you?

When was the last time you felt physical hunger?

On a scale of 1 to 10, how hungry are you right now?

Emotional Hunger

What are you feeling right now?

What would help this feeling?

What is missing in your life?

Mental Hunger

How often are you bored?

When did you last learn something new?

What would you enjoy learning?

Spiritual Hunger

How do you define your spirituality?

What increases your spirituality?

Are you living in congruence with your spiritual teachings?

Healing the Separation

Let's look deeper at each of our parts... *the physical, the emotional, the mental and the spiritual...* as we continue to heal the separation from Self.

Physical

Is your body a temple or a prison for your soul?

Our physical body needs healthy food to thrive.

What is our body? What should our body size be? Surely, some of us have felt the restriction of our body's weight and the obsessive thoughts about our weight. We have experienced the constant thoughts about how to control our weight, or we obsess about what to eat or not eat so our body will be a certain size. Maybe we haven't talked to a certain person or gone to an event because of our weight. Perhaps we chose an obsession with a diet or overeating over social interactions or a relationship.

Maybe we punished our Self for the overeating or for our weight. We may have used food, dieting, or the obsessive thoughts as a

---

means of avoiding living our lives. This can create a condition that becomes a bondage—a Self imposed prison.

Over the years, I have seen so many clients who have medical conditions caused by the over or under consumption of food. We created telephone sessions because we got *local* calls from clients who were not physically able to leave their homes because of their physical conditions.

By bringing the underlying reasons for using food into your awareness, you can change it. You cannot change anything until you are aware of it. You need to be aware of the results this has created for you in the past. Although this can be painful, it is the first step.

Emotional

Are your emotions on a runaway rollercoaster?

The best way to have the ability to care for our emotions is to be able to label the feelings. Then we can be aware of what we need. Food does not work for emotional needs. If we use food, we will create more negative feelings. We will bury the feelings we need to walk through. The only way to heal is to work through the feelings to get to the other side. If we don't acknowledge our feelings, they can surface in unexpected ways or erupt over trivial issues. Food can also affect our emotions.

Our emotional part needs awareness.

When I first started recovery, I found a startling awareness from my Chapter 2 Exercise, Examine the Binge Cycle. Every time I ate sugar, I felt depressed and tired a couple of hours later. I also had more urges to binge. Everyone is different. That is why it is important to find out for yourself what works for you and what does not work. No one could have made me *not* eat sugar. Even today, it is a choice. I know the consequences for my choices. At one time, I was not aware of the effects sugar had on me. I was on an emotional rollercoaster. It has been many years since I have rode that rollercoaster. I do not want to return to the sugar bondage again.

To know that we know what we know, and to know that we do not know what we do to not know, that is true knowledge.
-
Copernicus

Mental

"The greatest tool to change your world is your ability to change your thoughts."

Mentally, we need to be open to learning.

We put our Self in a prison by thinking *I know how to do this*. You're not going to really hear another possible solution if you have the answer and already think you know.

You do not know what it is that you don't know. If you knew that you didn't know, you could learn about it. However, if you do not even know what it is that you do not know, you cannot learn about that specific unknown. Think about that for a minute. Do you get it? Always keep an open mind; you will be surprised by what you will learn.

The only true wisdom is in knowing you know nothing. Socrates

There are so many new scientific discoveries happening every day. Science is opening up new ways of seeing the world. Just think, once we even thought the world was flat. People of that time did not know that the world was round and did not even question that for centuries.

We used to think the atom was the smallest particle. Then we found that in the atom there was a nucleus, and in the nucleus we found protons, neutrons, and electrons. We are not at the end of knowledge, but the beginning. You probably get the point. Be open to new ways of seeing the world and your Self.

Spiritual

"Spirituality is not religion, but it can be found in religion for some people."

The spiritual part of us needs spiritual food.

Sometimes, in order to understand spiritual hunger, we have to try some proven methods of nourishing the spiritual side of us so we can experience how this works. Prayers, meditation, being in nature, spiritual music, spiritual literature, making a gratitude list...these are just a few examples. We need to find our own path.

Spirituality is a connection we have with a Higher Power or God (as you understand God). As you get more connected to your

Self, you become more aware of your inner knowing or intuition. You will know what your truth is and what it is not. You become more accustomed to that *still small voice*. You can take in what is right for you and either disregard the rest or file it in your mind for future investigation. This is a very personal area, and it may take time to figure out what really works for you. It seems that once we start this investigation, the path becomes more and more clear. Try going to different places of worship and talking to other people about what works for them are excellent ways of gathering more information.

Summary for Healing the Separation

So how do we heal all these parts and bring our fragmented Self into wholeness? How do we get our 50 trillion individual intelligent cells to work together to form a healthy you? Think about this for a second; this community of you is alive. The cells in your body work together to help the community survive. Some of the cells come together to form the heart, or the liver, or our skin, and so forth. Then they work together to perform a function to keep our body healthy and alive. They mend and repair organs, filter out impurities, deteriorate and regenerate new cells. Our body has an inborn intelligence.

Neuroscience shows us that within each cell there is a molecular drama being played out in every cell. They tell us that emotions actually affect the drama within the cell and change the way cells behave. Cellular biologist, Dr. Masaru Emoto, photographed water crystals that had been exposed to different emotions and environments. The stunning photographs show how the crystals formed differently when exposed to different stimuli. Dr. Bruce H. Lipton describes in his book, *The Wisdom of Cells*, how our beliefs and thoughts alter the way the cellular drama is being played out in our bodies.

The food we eat is broken down into molecules that can feed each cell in this community of our living body. The body knows what nutrients are needed where and routes the nutrients to its destination.

One of the things I observed at the clinic was how profound the deficiency of adequate nutrients affected individuals. I saw people with anorexia lose their cognitive abilities. They seemed to be on an emotional roller coaster. I saw obese clients responding in the same way. Nutrients that the body can assimilate corrected this condition over time. What we put into our body matters! There is so much more at work than we realize. The human body is amazing. It will take care of us if we do the same.

Balance

All parts of our self needs to be in balance.

All these parts of Self require balance. When one or more parts are out of balance, it will affect the mind, body, emotions, and soul. The Self flourishes in a state of balance. When we look at a spiritual imbalance, we see disruptions in the mental, emotional, and physical Self as well. We know there is a connection between what we think and how we feel emotionally. We also know when we are depressed and dwell on negative emotions, these feelings can manifest in physical illness, both real and imagined.

The idea that an energy body surrounds the human form has endured since ancient times. Techniques such as *Kirlian photography* have now been used to photograph the portion of the energy body, which emanates from the fingertips or hands. Our Self is made up of energy. We need to be cautious of how much negativity to which we are exposed.

This can be experienced in the

- movies we watch,
- music we listen to,
- books we read,
- our home environment,
- our work environment, and the
- people we are around.

Become more aware of the energy in which you surround yourself. Have you ever been with someone and you just felt drained? Have you ever been in a cathedral, church, 12-Step meeting, or nature and felt peace? We have to balance the energies. The more negative spaces you occupy, the more positive experiences you need for balance. Let the light of the spirit shine on you, in you, and through you as much as possible.

Here is a list that can restore our internal balance:

- be in nature

- be part of a positive group consciousness

- really be present with another person

- play

- surround yourself with positive loving people

- laugh

- meditate

- just be

- be grateful

One amazing phenomenon that I have encountered with so many of my clients is that they have an extraordinary ability to pick up on energies. Most are not even aware of this because they attribute it to being too sensitive or defective in some way. I believe many people get into unhealthy ways of shielding themselves from this bombardment of feeling, emotions, and energy of things unseen or unexplained.

"Man knows more than he understands." -Alfred Adler

Have you ever walked into a room where two people were arguing? Could you *feel the tension in the air*? What if the people act like nothing is wrong? What do you believe, your intuitive feelings or what you see displayed? This is crazy making - at least you may think you are crazy or something is wrong with you. Is it any wonder we want to push our feelings out of our awareness?

In summary, when we use food or the obsessive thoughts of food, weight, or body image, we disconnect from our Self. We disconnect from our appetite and our internal guidance system. This makes us more vulnerable to allowing outside sources to control us. Because we do not have our own guidance system, we rely on diets, pills, drinks, and sugar to fix us. We lose touch with our Self.

> *"If you concentrate on finding whatever is good in every situation, you will discover that your life will suddenly be filled with gratitude, a feeling that nurtures the soul."*
> *-Rabbi Harold Kushner*

Diet's Don't Work®

CHAPTER EXERCISE: My Hunger Rating

Use the following scale before and after you eat to become more accustomed to your appetite and to see your eating patterns. For each meal, rate your hunger/satiation before and after eating.

	Description
0	Starving, stomach rumbling, lightheaded
1	You would eat anything you find, desserts, potato chips
2	Preoccupied with hunger, looking for fast food
3	Hungry, planning what or where to eat
4	Know you will be hungry soon, preparing a meal or arriving at a restaurant
5	Not hungry or full
6	Not hungry, but could eat more
7	Full, enjoyed the food. STOP HERE (you will be hungry again in 3 or 4 hours)
8	Stuffed, clothes feeling tight
9	Uncomfortable or mindless eating
10	Thanksgiving full, painful, maybe sick

In the following example, you started eating when you were hungry, planning what or where to eat (rating 3). Then you stopped when you were full and enjoyed the food (rating 7).

	Time	0	1	2	3	4	5	6	7	8	9	10
Example	7:30				X	X	X	X	X			
Meal 1												
Meal 2												
Meal 3												

© 2002 Rebecca Cooper   www.dietsdontwork.org   800-711-6336

CHAPTER EXERCISE: Food Effects

Use this chart when you suddenly become tired, sleepy, anxious, irritable, or depressed for no apparent reason. Check the possible food connections. Over time you may become aware of a food that prevents you from obtaining your goals. *This is valuable information for you .* You can then choose, instead of being controlled by the triggering effects of that food.

TIME	TIME OF LAST MEAL	REACTIONS AND OBSERVATIONS	POSSIBLE FOOD CONNECTIONS							MY FUTURE CHOICES
			S	F	C	FF	A	SF	O	

S= sugar;   F= fats;   C= carbohydrates including *flour*;   FF= fast foods;   A= alcohol;   SF= salty foods;   O= other: _____

© 2002 Rebecca Cooper

CHAPTER 4 ***Stuffing Your Feelings***

"Nobody can make you feel inferior without your consent."

Eleanor Roosevelt

Many emotional eaters are the kindest, most loving, sensitive people in this world. In fact, I believe most of them are more sensitive than the norm. They pick up on energies that others are not even aware of. Sometimes, they can have such an overwhelming response to a situation that they'll turn to food or other addictions just to lessen the external stimuli.

In this chapter, we'll explore the nature of our emotions and the patterns of stuffing feelings down with food or obsessive thoughts about dieting.

What Are Feelings?

Feelings are an emotional state or reaction. To learn more about our Self, we need to be able to label our feelings.

Take a look at the following chart. Major feelings are listed in the headers, and more descriptive emotional states are listed in the columns below.

Here are some words to describe feelings.

ANGRY	SAD	HAPPY	AFRAID	ASHAMED	HURT
Edgy	Mellow	Glad	Uncertain	Insecure	Disappointed
Crabby	Blue	Content	Uneasy	Inadequate	Upset
Annoyed	Somber	Pleased	Apprehensive	Vulnerable	Offended
Irritable	Moody	Amused	Concerned	Put Down	Dejected
Agitated	Gloomy	Cheerful	Anxious	Sorry	Disrespected
Angry	Discouraged	Joyful	Cautious	Apologetic	Shaken Up
Oppositional	Cheerless	Delighted	Worried	Embarrassed	Crushed
Defiant	Uncomfortable	Stoked	Doubtful	Guilty	Rejected
Mean	Unhappy	Excited	Tense	Demeaned	Agonized
Revengeful	Lonely	Jovial	Nervous	Remorseful	Used
Vindictive	Sorrowful	Optimistic	Distrustful	Regretful	Suffering
Devious	Heavyhearted	Overjoyed	Confused	Shameful	Insulted
Disgusted	Overwhelmed	Grateful	Perplexed	Humbled	Unloved
Aggressive	Depressed	Thrilled	Panicky	Humiliated	Punished
Belligerent	Pessimistic	Enthusiastic	Threatened	Sheepish	Vexed
Rebellious	Bitter	Elated	Dreadful	Debased	Battered
Enraged	Miserable	Blissful	Defenseless	Repentant	Abused
Provoked	Hopeless	Exultant	Scared	Stupid	Heartbroken
Livid	Desperate	Ecstatic	Horrified	Worthless	Violated

Figure 4.1: Words to Describe Feelings

What words describe your emotional state right now? Later, you will learn how the intensity of the feeling is linked to other situations.

Stuffing Our Feelings

Some of us have used food and obsessive thoughts around dieting, our weight, and our body image so often that we don't even know how to label a feeling. A feeling may surface, and we immediately replace it with food, action, obsessive thoughts, etc.

Some people try to *control* their feelings. The way they do this is usually to resist, ignore, reject, or repress them. Repressing your feelings does not eliminate them. Feelings never die. They refuse to be silenced. When you finally *forget* about a negative or unpleasant emotion, you may feel victorious, but the battle has just begun.

It takes a tremendous amount of emotional and physical energy or food to hold down your feelings. Trying to suppress our feelings or emotions becomes a struggle. As the suppressed emotions build, we have to fight to stay in control.

Repressed feelings can motivate much of our behavior. There are four ways that repressing feelings may affect you undesirably:

1. You may numb your ability to feel.
2. You may overreact to people or circumstances in the present.
3. You may insulate yourself from feeling by isolating, using disordered eating, or other addictions.
4. Your body may express the tension from holding on to repressed emotions through physical symptoms, weight gain, weight loss, stress, or disease.

Common Defenses against Feelings

The ways we repress feelings are many, and we call them *defenses*. Each defense serves as a way to avoid acknowledging and naming the feelings we are now experiencing. Basically, they prevent us from knowing what we are feeling.

Here is a list of common defense mechanisms. Do you recognize any of these?

☐ Arrogance	☐ Complying	☐ Apologizing	☐ Attacking
☐ Blaming	☐ Dominating	☐ Joking	☐ Criticizing
☐ Judging	☐ Moralizing	☐ Denial	☐ Defiance
☐ Evading	☐ Explaining	☐ Rationalizing	☐ Justifying

☐ Intimidating	☐ Minimizing	☐ Projecting	☐ Placating
☐ Interrogating	☐ Silence	☐ Controlling	☐ Withdrawing
☐ Sarcasm	☐ Intellectualizing	☐ Procrastinating	☐ Overworking

Figure 4.2: Common Defenses

Denial is the state of not being aware of our inner feelings, our inner fears, and our motivations. Self-awareness is the opposite of denial. Remember, *what we focus on gets bigger*. Sometimes our denial is so overpowering that we don't know ourselves anymore.

We lose the ability to connect to our self-awareness when certain triggers occur. Let's look at a few major defenses that prevent us from being aware. These defenses can come from others in our lives or from the way that we react.

A Closer Look

Let's take a closer look to discover how each defense has played a part in the separation from our self-awareness.

Control

Sometimes we have the false belief that we can control events or people. However, most of us have a hard time controlling ourselves, much less someone else. We get so caught up in the final outcome and making it happen. We lose ourselves in a frantic attempt to control. Our whole focus is on controlling the person or event. Have you ever made something happen only to find out that it wasn't what you wanted after all? Sometimes letting events unfold on their own pleasantly surprise us.

On the other hand, some of us give our power away. We let someone else control our lives, make all our decisions, and speak for us. They may heavily influence the Self we present to the world. After a while, we don't know where they end and we begin. We lose our Self. We also lose our ability to enjoy our life journey and be in the present.

Both forms of control require us to be out of touch with our True Self.

Manipulation

This defense can be summed up as the covert actions we take to get what we want without being direct. We may be so used to this defense that we don't even know we're using it. This is especially true if our assertiveness skills are lacking. Because we are afraid of asking for what we need or want, we may find a way to hint at our needs, ask indirectly, or develop elaborate schemes to accomplish our goals. It can take a lot of energy to circumvent being direct and assertive. If we are constantly manipulating our world, we don't have the time or energy to look at ourselves.

We can also be manipulated by others if we don't have a sense of Self or of our needs. If we are not connected to our feelings, we may not know that we're being manipulated. Manipulation always creates an uneasy feeling. Our feelings, therefore, can be a guidance system. If you sense something is wrong, you can choose to fix it or not. Not being aware of this manipulation can make us feel crazy. Someone else is directing your life. You feel like a puppet. If your life is full of manipulation, there is no room or time for your internal guidance system to grow.

Abuse

It has long been known that abuse can cause a person to shut out the experience by disassociation or separating from Self. These experiences have a profound effect on one's life. If we have abuse in our history, it is important to get professional help to work through the dislodged emotions.

Sometimes, because of the abuse, we don't like ourselves. This can be true of the abuser as well as the abused. To live a worthwhile life, we must get free of the damage that the abuse has caused. Abuse is usually an event in the past, a remembered hurt that is not happening now. We must reach out for help to stop it. It is hard to resolve this alone. Without help, it can take on a life of its own and stay in our mind as a present reminder. The abuser may be out of our life, but we are still recalling the abuse over and over and over again. So who is inflicting the mental abuse now?

Studies show that people with a negative self view are attracted to others who view them negatively, rather than someone who views them positively.[7]

I once left an abusive relationship. After that relationship ended, I spent some time alone with myself. One day I realized he was still in my head. He was physically gone, but I was talking to myself as he had talked to me. He was out of my life, but my condemning Self talk was just as bad. In time, I learned that we attract what we have inside us. He had been talking to me the way I was talking to myself. When I met him, he subconsciously felt familiar. I thought it must be love. It took some time to change my Self talk, but after I did, I was able to be in a wonderful partnership with another kind, loving soul.

Abandonment

Abandonment is a real or imagined loss of a loved one. If we have experienced abandonment in our history, we may be afraid to hurt like that again. We may wall off our emotions and not allow ourselves to be loved or to love. This can be bad enough, but sometimes we don't even love ourselves. We may think *if they didn't love us no one can*. In my opinion, abandonment of Self is the worst abandonment. Then we are really alone.

Freedom from Our Defenses

We can't change something we're not aware of.

How do we deal with the issues of control, manipulation, abuse, and abandonment? Have we used food or an obsession with dieting to deal with these problems? Have we repeated a pattern in our family or our lives?

We can't change something of which we're not aware. Because we push feelings from our consciousness with food and obsessive thoughts or behaviors, we don't even know what we feel or what is causing our feeling. And when we stuff our feelings, they seem to pop up unexpectedly.

---

[7] Hixon & Swann, 1993; Robinson & Smith-Lovin, 1992; Swann, Hixon, Stein-Seroussi, & Gilbert, 1990; Swann, Pelham, & Krull, 1989; Swann, Wenzlaff, Krull & Pelham, 1992

The way out is to understand *freedom*. Freedom is the ability to be your Self and to take care of yourself so that you are not being controlling, manipulative, abused, or disconnected from yourself (abandonment). It is taking care of your Self so that you do not dominate others, manipulate others, abuse others, or abandon yourself.

If any of these patterns has been part of our history, we need to look at how it is playing itself out in our life today. Then, with this awareness, we can change! We don't have to use food to push the feelings down. We don't have to be ruled by this any longer.

Independence means to not be dependent on a person or a thing for happiness. It means being able to depend on a Higher Power, your Inner Self, the Universal Goodness, or whatever you choose to call it. It can be a strength, power, or wisdom that can be with you always.

Independence is freedom. It means not being dependent on the opinions or expectations of others, not abandoning ourselves to please others. How many times have we used food – or the obsessive thoughts of food – because we were concerned about what someone thought about us? The truth is that these concerns are not real – they are only in our mind.

Reacting Instead of Responding

To change the way we feel at certain times, it can be helpful to be aware of what factors are influencing our feelings.

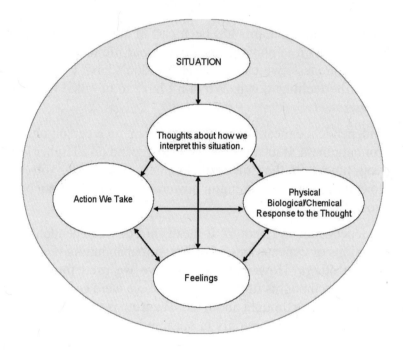

Figure 4.3: Understanding Our Feelings

Our thoughts, our biology, our emotions, and our behavior can interact and influence each other as well as our reaction to the situation. Even if we anticipate a situation, it can affect our responses. If our thoughts are potent enough, they may trigger biological changes that we may experience as emotions or feelings. These emotions, in turn, may influence our behavior, which may have an effect on the situations in our environment.

Sometimes a situation may create a feeling linked to a past event. If we are not aware of this *trigger*, we may experience feelings disproportionate to the particular situation. We may react instead of responding to the events in our life today.

Let's Look at an Example...

Situation: You pass someone in the hall.

Thoughts: This person looks just like your angry Aunt Betty from childhood.

Biology: You may experience certain biological changes, such as increased heart rate.

Emotion: You may or may not notice an angry feeling.

Behavior: The next person you talk to irritates you. If you're paying attention to your feelings, you may notice that your reaction seems out of proportion to their comments and actions. You can make a choice to consider this possibility, and decide not to act on your irritation. If you don't acknowledge your feelings, you may react or use food to escape from the confusing feeling.

Some Facts about Feelings

- There are no right or wrong feelings; feelings just are.
- No matter how strong a feeling is at first, it will pass.
- If feelings are ignored, they don't go away. They may manifest themselves in ways that can damage our relationships or our emotional, physical, or mental health.
- Our feelings can be mislabeled. We may think we feel angry when, in fact, we may actually be hurt or afraid.
- If we do not accept and express our feelings honestly and appropriately, we may use food to cover them up.
- Feelings will not kill you.

When our emotional reaction is out of proportion with a situation, this can be a clue that we might be reacting to past feelings that we have stuffed. This can be a helpful tool in discovering whether the past is still playing a part in our life today.

Relative Intensity of Words	Feeling Category				
	Anger	Conflict	Fear	Happiness	Sadness
Mild Feeling	Perturbed Annoyed Bothered Bugged Irked Irritated	Questioning Caught Caught in a bind Pulled Unsure	Apprehensive Concerned Tense Tight Uneasy	Amused Comfortable Confident Contented Glad Pleased	Apathetic Bored Confused Disappointed Discontented Mixed up Resigned
Moderate Feeling	Angry Disgusted Harassed Mad Provoked Put upon Resentful Set up Spiteful Used	Catch-22 Locked Pressured Torn Blocked Bound	Afraid Alarmed Anxious Fearful Frightened Threatened Worried	Delighted Eager Happy Hopeful Joyful Surprised Up moved Proud	Discouraged Distressed Down Drained Empty Hurt Lonely Sad Unhappy
Intense Feeling (Examine possible links to past events.)	Betrayed Sabotaged Exploited Contemptuous Enraged Fuming Furious Hateful Infuriated Pissed	Trapped Ripped Wrenched Suffocated Resentment Vengeful Abused Tortured	Desperate Overwhelmed Panicky Petrified Scared Terrified Terror-stricken	Bursting Ecstatic Elated Enthusiastic Fulfilled Thrilled Turned on	Anguished Depressed Despairing Helpless Hopeless Miserable Overwhelmed Smothered Tortured Grief-stricken

Figure 4.4: Feeling Intensity Chart

Tools for Dealing with Feelings

Here are some helpful tools for dealing with your feelings. See which ones will work for you.

Just let it be. When a feeling comes up, become aware of it. Sit with it. *Own* it and go through it. Let it be. Feelings are just feelings. They are not negotiable.

Name the feeling. Evaluate if the intensity level is in proportion to the incident.

Breathe. Have you noticed how shallow your breathing becomes when you become upset? When you have a difficult feeling, take several slow, deep breaths. This will center you.

Remember that you don't have to act on your feelings. Having a feeling doesn't mean you have to do anything about it right now or ever. Feelings can just be felt. All feelings are okay.

Don't judge feelings. Your feelings are automatically justified, just because you feel them...even if no one else validates them. Your feelings are neither right nor wrong; there are no *shoulds* when it comes to feelings.

Notice negative tapes. Take a moment out to *re-program* your internal computer. Hear yourself when the *critical* parent kicks in. You can *retrain your brain*. Tell yourself nurturing things. Be a loving, kind parent to your *inner child*.

Stay in the moment. Often we *project into the future* or *fall into the past*. We then have a tendency to create negative projections for the future, or we fall into depression or anxiety by bringing it into the present. Allow yourself to accept the present as the gift that it is.

Check out reality. Because our most difficult feelings are either based in fear from the past or future projections, they can have little to do with our current reality. Talk with an objective, emotionally safe person. One acronym of fear is False Evidence Appearing Real.

Remember, *This too shall pass.* Feelings, like cravings, are temporary. No matter how uncomfortable you may feel, the feelings will pass in time.

Let your feelings thaw out. If you blocked your feelings off as a child, you may be emotionally numb now, no longer even aware of what you feel. As you heal, you may be in for some surprises – the feelings will surface. Getting in touch with your feelings is a process. It may take a bit of time. When you've been numb all your life, it takes a while to thaw out. Be gentle with your Self.

Get professional help if you need assistance moving through all of the surfacing feelings. You also could join a local or internet support group.

It is difficult to decide on an alternate action in the moment the feeling arises. You need to decide ahead of time what action would be best. This action must be your decision, not something you think you <u>should</u> do. See what works for you, and then start practicing this action instead of going to the food. This is another place you can break the binge cycle. (See Figure 2.2)

DietsDon'tWork®

CHAPTER EXERCISE: Actions for Feelings

Feeling	What Actions could help me?
Anger	
Lonely	
Bored	
Fearful	
Frustrated	
Stressed	
Tired	

© 2009 Rebecca Cooper

www.dietsdontwork.org

800-711-6336

CHAPTER 5 *Change Your Thinking, Change Your Life*

"Your life becomes what you think."
-Marcus Aurelius

We use communication to build relationships. Since we're working on re-connecting with the Self, let's take a look at the communication going on within us. We can find this dialogue in our thoughts.

Remember, what we focus on gets bigger

Self-Talk

Our thoughts dramatically influence the way we feel and behave. In fact, the power of your thoughts can change your life. Olympic athletes, musicians, golfers, and many others rehearse in their minds, accomplishing the feat perfectly and succeeding with the goal of winning. Rather than visualizing just winning, they feel the feelings of the victory. Studies have shown this type of practice produces results.

Negative thinking takes away energy that could be used to accomplish our goals.

Can you imagine what would happen if these same people dwelled on thoughts of negativity, such as *I can't do it, I'm no good*, and *I'll never win*? This type of thinking produces results as well, but not the good ones we're going for.

Negative thinking takes away energy that could be used to accomplish our goals. If we're always telling ourselves that we can't do it, we will always be struggling. Life becomes harder than it should be. Imagine trying to do something when someone is always pointing out the negatives. Most of us would just give up or, better yet, get away from that person. But if that person is our Self, there is no place to go to get away.

What if, as an alternative, we had someone who kept encouraging us, pointing out all of our successes, and congratulating us? Wouldn't we be more likely to keep moving ahead with ease and enthusiasm?

What you can do, or dream you can do, begin it; boldness has genius, power, and magic in it. -Johann von

You have a choice. What self-talk do you want to focus on to attain your goals? Encouraging self-talk, of course! When working on creating more positive self-talk, imagine that your habitual thoughts are like repeating a prayer over and over again. "I'm so fat." "I'm so fat". So what if your prayers are being answered? This is where you have been spending your mental and emotional energy. Negative thinking takes away energy that could be used to accomplish our goals.

Fix your thoughts on what is true, good and right. Think about things that are pure, and lovely... Philippians 4:8

We can't *not* think about something. *For example, don't think of a yellow banana. Whatever you do, just don't think of a yellow banana! What are you thinking about? What's the <u>only</u> thing you can think about? A yellow banana of course!* In the moment we think about what we don't want to think about, our mind pictures it, so we need to replace an unwanted thought with the opposite and allow that thought to grow. The other thought will automatically be replaced.

The Second Thought

Many of us would never treat or talk to a friend in the negative manner that we treat and talk to our Self. We usually cannot control the first thought that comes to our mind. Being aware, however, of our thinking gives us a choice. We can consciously change a thought. We don't have to dwell on a disturbing thought; we can switch the station and go to another channel. Remember, what we focus on gets bigger.

See the habitual first negative thought as a red flag. It can alert us to substitute the second thought. We then can focus on the thinking conducive to our desired experience. If we don't like the experiences we are getting, we must change our habitual thoughts. The environment or effects of our thoughts will change naturally.

We can alter our environment, but unless we alter our thoughts, the new environment, relationship, or job will become much like the old one. Our thoughts create our reality.

The best way to heal our sabotaging self-talk is to be a master of the second thought. Here are some examples of going to *a second thought*:

First Thought	Second Thought
Food	Am I physically hungry? On a scale of 1-10, where am I?
Parents	Is this my truth or theirs? Write a letter. Sending it is optional.
Spouse/mate	Journaling your feelings is a way to clarify feelings. This will make any conversation more meaningful.
The future/the past	Where am I right now? Be fully present to the experience of now.
Responsibilities/ Overwhelmed	Make a "To-Do List" and mark off each item as you complete it.
Feelings	Name the feeling and identify your corresponding tool to help it.
Fear	Prayer. Remember the fears you have walked through already.
Anxiety	Take deep breaths. The mind will tell the body that it is relaxed.
I always fail!	Examine the evidence – have you always failed? Remember some of your successes.

Be a master of the second thought.

Figure 5.1: Master of the Second Thought

Let's consider some common ways our thinking gets distorted.

Distorted Thinking

You can never be too thin is a popular saying we echo in our minds. Some have actually died in the pursuit of being that *perfectly thin person.* Someone's thinking can become so distorted that they block out their natural desire to preserve the physical body. In that same pursuit, some of us become so discouraged that our sabotaging behaviors lead us into obesity.

Let's examine some of the other thinking that sabotages us.

Care-taking: It is a common characteristic of emotional eaters to help everyone else while ignoring their own needs. This can be a way of avoiding what is bothering us. When we are reaching for food, and we are not physically hungry, some part of our Self is asking for help. We need to be loving and *learn to take care of what is <u>really</u> bothering us.*

Overgeneralization: A specific event is seen as being characteristic of life in general, rather than as being one event among many. Some examples of this way of thinking are I *always overeat*, I *never* do anything right, and I *never* do that.

Judgment: Someone assumes that others are thinking negatively toward them without evidence that this is the case. *People avoid me because they think I'm fat*, they might conclude, for instance. Couldn't this kind of thought cause you to be less approachable? We might also think *that person is pretty and trim, and she has never had a problem with food. Her life is perfect.* Or we may think *she is your typical gorgeous blonde.*

Fortune-telling: This person acts as though her negative expectations about the future are established facts. Her thoughts could be *I'm going to be just like my mother, I've never been able to keep weight off before, this time will be no different,* or *I'll never get what I want.*

Emotional reasoning: In this distortion, the person assumes that emotional reactions necessarily reflect the true situation. Remember, feelings just are. They're not right or wrong, and you do not have to live your life based on passing feelings. Know that the feelings will pass. We don't have to act on every feeling. We don't have to eat to get rid of a feeling. The feeling and craving will pass on its own. It can be helpful to give your Self ten minutes (perhaps journal what you are thinking) before you eat. You may then see that the need to eat has passed along with the feeling.

Non-motivational rules: The uses of *should, have to,* or *must* statements to provide motivation and control behavior seem to accomplish the exact opposite. Such self-talk can sabotage us. *I should exercise every day.* How motivating is that? *Should* comes from the external environment and not listening to our inner Self. *I want* comes from inside. We rebel from external forms of control, but are motivated by internal cues.

Labeling or judgments: The distortion here is in attaching a global label to oneself, rather than referring to a specific event or action. We think *I'm a failure* rather than *I made a mistake.* This form of thinking puts us at a different level than others. We're above or below the other person and it prevents us from connecting to others.

Failure is the opportunity to begin again more intelligently.
-Henry Ford

Overwhelmed thinking: We may get so caught up in all the things we have to do that we never even start. To think, *I need to write this book* can feel more overwhelming than *my goal is to write one chapter a month.* Now that the book is in process, I can manage one chapter at a time. Adjusting overwhelming thoughts can help us attain our dreams and goals.

Perfectionism or unrealistic expectations: What is the perfect body or perfect person? We see others in the media or in real life, and we perceive their appearance as a goal for us to strive for. We compare our inferior insides or outsides to what we believe is their perfect projection. But what we don't realize is that a lot of these so-called *ideal* people feel the same as we do on the inside and may be practicing very unhealthy behaviors.

Better to do something imperfectly than to do nothing flawlessly.
- Robert Schuller

We may feel incompetent to accomplish a challenging task, so we don't even attempt it for fear of failure. If we can't do an outstanding job, then we don't want to even try. When we postpone anything until we are perfect, we postpone our lives. We are not living life to the fullest, but living in some sort of limbo.

Living life to the fullest means making mistakes.

Living life to the fullest means making mistakes. We learn from our mistakes. It's ironic that making mistakes is where we learn. That's the practice that really brings us closer to perfection. Most dreams are realized only after several attempts. In the failing, we learn what does not work. We proceed with baby steps. Always building toward our dreams even when we retreat a step, we are still on the path to our dreams. We cannot accomplish anything by waiting to be perfect.

Procrastination: Sometimes we use food to block ourselves from doing life. There may be something we need to do, but we just don't want to do it right now, so we focus on the food as a way of blocking ourselves from the actions we need to take. On the other hand, we may not feed our body when we are physically hungry. We might continue to stay busy to avoid eating. We rationalize that we'll eat after finishing what we're doing. Then we get busy doing something else. We may have waited so long to eat that when we do eat, we binge.

Black or white thinking: It's either everything or nothing; it's black or it's white, with no shades of grey. For instance, we may have a bite of a *forbidden food* or have eaten a little too much and think, *I've blown it, so I might as well binge.*

Control fallacies: When we focus on controlling *everything,* we get so overwhelmed that we actually end up having less control. It becomes a relief when we learn the things we really *can* control and do a good job with that. A lot of the time we find the only thing we can control is our attitude. Some of us get caught in the control fantasy of thinking that if we can control our eating, not eating, or weight, we are in control of our lives. This can be a way of being in denial of life situations.

Blaming or victimization: Sometimes we play the *blame game* or see ourselves as victims. We focus on someone or something else that we think are causing our problems. This leaves us powerless to change the situation because we cannot change someone else. We can only change ourselves. Wasting our energy on blame or victimization prevents our own progress.

Personalization: Here we see ourselves as the cause of a particular event, when in fact other factors *are* responsible. This differs from taking responsibility in a positive way. We start beating ourselves up for situations that are not our fault. This leaves us with no energy to accomplish our goals.

See how distorted thinking creates the need to just check out, or to get some relief by eating. We may turn to food just to stop this crazy pattern of thinking. So how do we change it?

What Leads to a Changed Mindset

We start the day by connecting with our Self. We can do this by getting quiet; meditating, praying, walking, journaling, or whatever works for you to access your inner Self. This way, you can start the day from your true center.

*What if we had someone who kept encouraging us, pointing out all our successes, and congratulating us? That someone can be **you**!*

We can get clear about what is really most important in our life. Isn't it amazing how our preoccupation with food, weight, and body size prevents us from living the life we want?

As we connect back to ourselves, we learn what brings us joy. As we travel on this path to our inner Self, we learn our life's meaning and purpose. We learn what our passions are, and things that we really love to do.

To avoid the overwhelm trap, break down your goals into manageable steps- start with baby steps. Determine the very first thing you need to do. This is the hardest part of accomplishing anything. But once you start, the momentum will carry you forward. You build on your successes.

We give thanks and congratulate ourselves for every step of the way. This keeps the ball rolling. Remember, *what we focus on gets bigger.*

We write a *What I Am Grateful For* list in our journal. It's amazing how this can change your mental perspective. When you know what you are grateful for, it is easier to focus on the positive and let those thoughts grow.

It's important to remember that you are doing the best you can at any point in time. As your awareness grows, your thinking and behavior will change.

As a result of your growing self-awareness, you'll come to know what your capabilities and limitations are. You'll know where you excel and where you need assistance. You won't be afraid to ask for help and will be willing to learn new things. You'll become less vulnerable to outside pressures because you'll know your Self. The more self-awareness you develop, the freer you'll be to make your own choices.

The Path Out of Disordered Eating

Every action starts with a thought, conscious or not.

We now understand that many of us use food to push down feelings. Our disordered eating is in response to a feeling starting to surface. A feeling is often an indicator of a thought. We need to be aware of the thoughts we are thinking. We need to get familiar with what our primary thoughts are. The more associations you can find between thoughts and certain feelings, the more prepared you are to deal with them. You can't change something for which you are not even aware. If you think *I'm not going to think about the problem*, you are thinking about the problem. You must find a replacement thought, action, prayer, or affirmation.

Our thoughts become habits with practice, just like our actions. Everything we do or think could be the formation of a habit.

"For as he thinketh in his heart, so he is." Proverbs 23:7

When the conscious mind accepts an idea, it begins to put it into action. It mobilizes subconscious resources you don't even know you possess. This can be used for good or bad. Your constant thoughts create your reality. What if you constantly thought *I can't do this. I will fail.* You will fail. What chances would you have at succeeding if you are always focusing on failing? We need positive habitual thoughts coupled with the emotions of succeeding to produce positive results. Athletes and musicians practice their performance in their mind constantly. They know the power this mindset can create. So how do you see yourself? What are you telling yourself?

Practice affirmations. It can take a long time to change self-talk that we have been using for years. Write down your current self-talk, and come up with an affirmation for it. Practice saying the affirmations in a mirror. Some say the eyes are the windows of the soul. When you say something positive to your Self in the mirror, it seems to really get in. Make the affirmations believable, positive, and in the present tense. You don't want to be in a state of wanting or waiting for it in the future.

A miracle is a shift in perception. -The Course in Miracles

Feelings propel thoughts into reality. Your subconscious doesn't know if your thoughts or situations are real or imagined. Feel what it feels like to believe your affirmation. Then watch for the results.

Obstacles to Growth and Joy

1. Attachment to our will
2. Being rigid in our expectations
3. Thinking we know it all
4. Pride and ego running our life
5. Assuming the responsibilities of others
6. Perfectionism
7. Thinking only of our Self
8. Being untrue to our Self
9. Hurting Self or Others
10. Being judgmental
11. Not having a meaning or purpose in our life
12. Unclean living or anything that interferes with the health of the body, mind, soul or others
13. Habitual negative thinking
14. Living in fear

Some Things to Think On:

- Your thoughts determine your feelings.
- Your beliefs about your Self and the world are a system of organized thoughts that you tell your Self over and over.
- You can be a prisoner of your own thinking and unchallenged beliefs.
- The only reality is *now*. The past is over; the future is not here yet.
- You can consciously develop your ability to eliminate unwanted thoughts and feelings at will.
- You determine how you choose to see a situation.
- Negative thoughts are like weeds in a garden. Unless they are plucked, they will tend to overtake your consciousness.
- You can live your life without living *in* your thoughts.
- While you may have been victimized by circumstances, you are the only one who can determine whether you will remain a victim.
- You can choose to live in love rather than fear.
- Your happiness is a function of eliminating your negative thinking.
- Trying to change another person through control and blame never works.
- The world is your mirror. What you dislike in other people is usually what you don't like about your Self, now or in the past.

Figure 5.2: Things to Think On

Thoughts held in mind produce after their kind.
-Charles Fillmore

One Minute to Think

In one of my groups, I had my clients take a minute to just be quiet and be present with themselves. They were told ahead of time that they will be writing down those thoughts. Here is what they came up with.

> What am I supposed to do?
> What does she want me to write?
> I don't understand.
> I can't do anything right!
> Oh well, just another failure.
> My thighs are so big!
>
> I am so tired.
> My coworker was so mean to me.
> I have to workout now.
> I bet the traffic will be bad!
> I am so overwhelmed.
> I have no time.
> I'm hungry!
>
> This is ridiculous.
> I have better things to do.
> I don't want to be here.
> What will I do after this?
> I want to smoke or eat while I think about it.

Notice their thought process. In all three examples, they went from negative thinking to disordered eating thoughts. If they had not been in a group, each said the next step would have been to eat even thought they were not physically hungry.

How many of these thoughts were positive? Notice if your thoughts lead you to thoughts of food, weight, diet, or body image.

We can't change something for which we are not aware, and many of us are not even aware of what we are thinking or saying

---

to ourselves. We know our thoughts contribute to emotional eating. Now change is possible.

Diets Don't Work®

CHAPTER EXERCISE: Changing Self Talk

What do I say to Self?	What do I wish to say to Self?

© 2000 Rebecca Cooper

www.dietsdontwork.org

800-711-6336

CHAPTER 6 *Exploring Your Beliefs & Values*

"I have found the greatest help in meeting my problem with decency and self-respect and whatever courage is demanded, is to know where you yourself stand. That is, to have in words what you believe you are acting from."

- William Faulkner

What Do You Believe?

Beliefs form the filter through which we look at our world. Let's say I grew up in South America. When I was about 10 years old, I got a pet snake, Oscar. I watched Oscar for hours and could even play with him. Then, I left South America and became an adult. One beautiful day in the Caribbean, I went to dinner with my friends. We were all seated and ready to order. I looked to my right. I saw a little snake slither under the door coming into the restaurant. It looked just like Oscar. Warm beautiful memories

"Nothing is either good or bad. It's thinking that makes it so."
-Benjamin Franklin

flooded over me, but then I heard a scream, and then another. Pandemonium broke out all because of the tiny snake. I walked over and picked it up as people climbed onto their chairs. It was very apparent that my belief about this snake was different from the rest of the patrons. Because of their beliefs, they felt fear. It was the same snake; our filters were just different.

Our beliefs are the building blocks for our thoughts. Our beliefs propel our thoughts into feelings. Your beliefs govern your thoughts and feelings. You act and make decisions based on your beliefs and values. Most of us have never taken the time to really look at what we believe or value. Our whole life is based on this filter. It affects every aspect of our life.

We may have put labels on ourselves that were not correct.

Mahatma Gandhi said, "Man often becomes what he believes himself to be. If I keep on saying to myself that I cannot do a certain thing, it is possible that I may end by really becoming incapable of doing it. On the contrary, if I have the belief that I can do it, I shall surely acquire the capacity to do it even if I may not have it at the beginning." Our conscious mind carries out the will of the subconscious. Since the subconscious mind may resist attempts to change our habits, it's helpful to get to know this underlying operating system. We need to evaluate the effectiveness of the beliefs that drive us. A clear healthy subconscious can be a spectacular inner-guide. It gives us good information that helps us to make decisions, and it gives us a sense of security.

"In certain moments a single almost insignificant sorrow may, by association, bring together all the little relics of pain and discomfort, bodily and mental, that we have endured even from infancy."
- Samuel Taylor Coleridge

Subconscious Beliefs

We may have formed beliefs that hold us back in our lives.

When we believe something, we are convinced that a certain proposition is true. The danger is that we can buy into an idea, even though it is completely false or not even our own. These false beliefs can include limiting beliefs that hold us back in our lives. A belief held in the subconscious can conflict with an intention we consciously are pursuing. To heal and grow, we need to bring limiting subconscious beliefs into our awareness so they can be re-examined.

Some of us have had things happen to us in our life that we intuitively knew were wrong. We placed labels on ourselves that were not correct. We believed we were wrong, bad, or unloved. We formed beliefs for which we are not even aware. Those beliefs are part of our daily life. We may now be acting on these beliefs from our core subconscious level.

"You cannot depend on your eyes when your imagina- tion is out of focus." *-Mark Twain*

Sometimes, as children, we were given standards, values, beliefs, or morals that were impossible to live up to in real life. Some- times we were given *double messages*. We were told that certain actions were wrong, but they were shown to be acceptable through modeled behaviors. As an example; being told not to smoke cigarettes or get drunk while watching our caregiver smoke or become intoxicated; or being sent to church instead of taken, while a parent stayed home. Sometimes we have been given beliefs or morals from someone who was struggling with their own issues.

Subconsciously, we will take actions to fulfill our expectations. What do you really expect will happen? You need to believe there is hope and believe that change is possible. Start asking yourself what you truly believe.

"In the providence of mind, what one believes to be true, either is true or becomes true." *-John Lilly*

Today is a good day to sort out your beliefs, and take a good look at what you really believe in. What beliefs are good for you and which ones are harming you? We'll be looking at both beliefs and values closely in the Chapter Exercise.

Commonly Held Limiting Beliefs

Have you felt trapped in a prison of limitations? In order to be true to our real self, we need to spend time examining and challenging our limiting beliefs. Could any of the following be part of your current belief system? Check all that apply.

- ☐ Material things denote my worth.
- ☐ If my partner really knew me, he would leave.
- ☐ I need him or her.
- ☐ I'll make a fool of myself if I try something new.
- ☐ I never finish anything.
- ☐ People are users.
- ☐ Give a little, and they'll want a lot.
- ☐ If I eat one, I'll binge.
- ☐ I never lose the weight, nothing works.
- ☐ Nice guys finish last.
- ☐ People take advantage of nice people.
- ☐ Do unto them, before they do it to you.
- ☐ Love hurts.
- ☐ Love never lasts.
- ☐ I will be just like Mom.
- ☐ Everyone loses their figure when they get old.
- ☐ It's natural for men to be unfaithful.
- ☐ Girls are shallow and catty.
- ☐ Men only want one thing.
- ☐ You have to work hard to achieve anything in life.
- ☐ Achievers have to sacrifice good relationships.
- ☐ The world is getting more corrupt.
- ☐ You can't trust anyone.
- ☐ Family is all that counts.

Figure 6.1: Limiting Beliefs

What about trying some of the following?

- ▪ Everything happens for a reason.
- ▪ I believe in miracles.

- Love is all around me.

- I am confident and secure.

- I am so lucky.

- My body is perfect just as it is.

- I attract healthy loving people.

What if we lived our life according to this second set of beliefs? Our lives can change when we become mindful of our beliefs and values, and change those that are not working for us. How do we accomplish this?

- Replacing limiting beliefs with supportive ones

- Practicing affirmations

- Reading uplifting spiritual literature

- Being around others of a desired mindset

- Being in touch with what's going on in our mind

What Are My Spiritual Beliefs?

Sometimes our spiritual beliefs can be the hardest part to look at. We may have been raised in a religion where it was not acceptable to question the rules, doctrines, or beliefs. Start investigating your belief in a universal energy, God, Higher Power, or whatever fits for you. Is this power a presence that can help you or does it condemn you? Is it a loving or fearful higher power? Find a Higher Power you can work with. Substitute the word God, Higher Power, loving universe, or whatever works for you to stop the negative thoughts. You are beginning to practice the presence of God. The more you substitute the idea of a loving God, the weaker the disordered thoughts become. Forcing or trying does not work; only practice works! Be open to a solution to the problem, maybe one you haven't even thought of. Believe all things are a part of a valuable soul lesson and your Higher Power knows the whole lesson, including the best solution. Look for the miracle, coincidence, and synchronicity in finding the solutions.

"Live your beliefs and you can turn the world around."
- Henry David Thoreau

Watch how the solutions flow. They will be happening all around you. You just have to be out of the obsessive disordered thinking to see them.

Affirm your Self and God with each noticed coincidence or miracle. Think about this when another problem emerges. Think about what is the next action step I can take. The most effective actions come from a calm mind. Meditate, pray, journal, and allow the creative force inside you to present solutions. Check out your solutions with a mentor, sponsor, parent, or someone you respect. If it comes to you three times from three different sources, chances are good that it is the path to take.

When I was growing up with my grandparents in the Bible Belt I became very confused. The pastor would scream from the pulpit that we would burn in hell if we disobeyed the church doctrine. We had to wear dresses below the knees. It was a sin to watch TV or go to the movies, play cards, and you were really bad if you were with boys, drank alcohol, or smoked. Everything was fine until I turned thirteen. Then I heard I would even go to hell if I had impure thoughts. That did it! I knew I was going to burn in hell so I may as well go for it. I turned my back on God. Ironically, I also started in my eating disorder at age 13. It was many years later and a lot of heartache and pain before I found my way back to a spirituality that works. This is not to condemn religion. It was just my perception of what I interpreted at that time. Many people find their spirituality in religion. That was just not my path.

Over the years, the subject of spirituality has been so important for my clients' recovery. Most have lost any connection to spirituality because they thought they were bad or unworthy. They ask, *why didn't God remove this horrible obsession with food or an eating disorder?*

One of the best solutions for eating disorder recovery is to stop allowing the external to control you. What better solution can there be? Turning internally to a loving connection with their spirituality and God or Higher Power can create miracles. There, they have access to all the strength, wisdom, direction, and companionship that they so desperately need.

When investigating spirituality, many clients were able to talk for the first time about what they believed. I will list some of these here. Most ideas here are not traditional. Please read them and see what rings true for you. Take what you like and disregard the rest, but please do not take offense. This was part of our journey and yours may be very different. We do not have all the answers, but we are searching for a spirituality that works for recovery from disordered eating.

1. Many cultures and people have different names for God or a Higher Power.
2. We have an internal knowing of when we are being exposed to truth. When we disconnect from our internal Self, we lose this barometer.
3. Trusting our complete spiritual direction to someone else prevents us from finding our own way.
4. Our connection to God is a direct internal connection between our soul and God or a Higher Power.
5. The God-spirit can help us and work through us to help others if we let it.
6. The God-spirit is positive universal energy present in each atom.
7. Spiritual energy is more pronounced in nature, houses of worship, spiritually-consciousness gatherings, art, music, beauty, and the like.
8. A group of like-minded people with the intent of spiritual development form a group consciousness.
9. A group consciousness can give rise to more awareness than possible individuality.
10. A critical mass group consciousness can change the world.
11. Our constant thoughts with the fuel of feeling become our prayers.
12. Habitual negative thoughts can put our soul in bondage.
13. The disconnection from the Self-Soul-Spirit can lead to addictions of many kinds.
14. Anything you put ahead of your God-connection can become an addiction.
15. Faith is intent fueled by belief of the desired outcome.

16. If we are looking for and believing in miracles, they occur all the time.
17. Evil is fueled by negative, harmful, egotistical thoughts, conscious or not.
18. Hardships are an opportunity to help us and others learn, grow, and heal the past.
19. The greatest gift is to be able to love unconditionally and accept unconditional love.
20. We are here to help ourselves and others to connect to our own internal divine Self so we may love ourselves and be able to love others as our Self.

Being True to Me

Our values – ideas we consider worth honoring – reflect our True Selves. Values are our core beliefs. When our behavior conflicts with our values, it leads to guilt and poor self-worth, which sets us up to fall into unhealthy patterns. It's important to consciously establish your values – instead of just following what is dictated by your parents, others, or the media.

Our life is woven by our thoughts that arise out of our values and beliefs. We live according to our values. We use our values to measure new beliefs. How closely do you measure up to your values and beliefs? Can you see that you use your values and beliefs to judge yourself and others?

Knowing Your Values

Which of these values have been tested as you walk through your life's experiences?

Our parents, teachers, peers, and others influence us to create values that we hold near and dear. Some of these values are never tested. The test comes when we are challenged to prove ourselves to ourselves. For instance, how far will we go to prove our honesty? Will we cheat on our taxes? Do we return found money? How often do we say what we mean? Can we be counted on to provide aid when the need is presented? Do we dig deeper into our wallets for a worthy cause? Do we write a letter to a congressman to improve our system? Do we speak up about an injustice?

Our behaviors provide a foundation for whom and what we say we value. In other words, we prove ourselves by living up to the values we say we have. We are at peace and congruent with our actions and values.

Many of these behaviors have been taken unconsciously. This is why knowing our values give us the power to be true to our Self on a conscious level. Please take your time as you review your life through this new lens. It is important that you identify the strengths you've used as you behaved in ways that were congruent with the values you say you have. Dig deeply into your life for it will provide you with great foundation for future decision-making.

LIST OF VALUES

Below is a list of values that you can use to identify your own value system. Ask yourself if this is your value or someone else's. Check the ones that apply to you. Think about the behaviors that you do to demonstrate your values. You can decide to live up to that value or take it off the list.

☐ Accountability	☐ Freedom	☐ Purity
☐ Achievement	☐ Friendship	☐ Quality
☐ Aspiration	☐ Generosity	☐ Reliability
☐ Beauty	☐ Gratitude	☐ Respect
☐ Challenge	☐ Harmony	☐ Responsibility
☐ Change	☐ Health	☐ Risk
☐ Cleanliness	☐ Honesty	☐ Safety
☐ Cooperation	☐ Honor	☐ Security
☐ Collaboration	☐ Humility	☐ Selflessness
☐ Commitment	☐ Industry	☐ Serenity
☐ Community	☐ Integrity	☐ Service
☐ Compassion	☐ Joyfulness	☐ Simplicity
☐ Creativity	☐ Justice	☐ Sincerity
☐ Decisiveness	☐ Knowledge	☐ Skill
☐ Democracy	☐ Leadership	☐ Spirituality
☐ Detachment	☐ Loyalty	☐ Stability
☐ Determination	☐ Love	☐ Status
☐ Growth	☐ Mobility	☐ Strength
☐ Graciousness	☐ Moderation	☐ Success
☐ Discipline	☐ Money	☐ Timeliness
☐ Diversity	☐ Patience	☐ Temperance
☐ Equality	☐ Peace	☐ Tolerance
☐ Excellence	☐ Perfection	☐ Tradition
☐ Efficiency	☐ Persistence	☐ Truth
☐ Fairness	☐ Power	☐ Trust
☐ Faith	☐ Prosperity	☐ Wellness
☐ Family	☐ Punctuality	☐ Wisdom
☐ Flexibility	☐ Purposefulness	

Summary

We know from experience that we have to live in accordance with our beliefs and values. We cannot be true to our Self if we are out of alignment with these. We first need to be aware of what we truly believe and what we do value. Then we determine if we are in alignment with them.

We then have two choices. We either have to change our belief or value, or we need to bring our Self into alignment with them. We cannot feel comfortable any other way. Food is often used to push this misalignment from our conscious mind. This is an important step toward recovery.

OUR DEEPEST FEAR IS NOT THAT WE ARE INADEQUATE.
OUR DEEPEST FEAR IS THAT WE ARE
POWERFUL BEYOND MEASURE.

IT IS OUR LIGHT, NOT OUR DARKNESS THAT MOST
FRIGHTENS US.

WE ASK OURSELVES, "WHO AM I TO BE BRILLIANT,
GORGEOUS, TALENTED AND FABULOUS?"

ACTUALLY, WHO ARE YOU NOT TO BE?

YOU ARE A CHILD OF GOD.
YOUR PLAYING SMALL DOESN'T SERVE THE WORLD.

THERE IS NOTHING ENLIGHTENED ABOUT SHRINKING SO
THAT OTHER PEOPLE WON'T FEEL INSECURE AROUND YOU.

WE WERE BORN TO MANIFEST THE GLORY OF GOD
THAT IS WITHIN US.

IT'S NOT JUST IN SOME OF US; IT'S IN EVERYONE.

AND AS WE LET OUR OWN LIGHT SHINE, WE UNCONSCIOUSLY
GIVE OTHER PEOPLE PERMISSION TO DO THE SAME.

AS WE ARE LIBERATED FROM OUR OWN FEAR,
OUR PRESENCE AUTOMATICALLY LIBERATES OTHERS.

Nelson Mandela, 1994

Diets Don'tWork®

CHAPTER EXERCISE- Self Alignment

Belief	Revised Belief
Value	Revised Value

©2009 Rebecca Cooper

www.dietsdontwork.org

800-711-6336

CHAPTER 7

Boundaries

"One Always receiving, never giving, is like a stagnant pool, in which whatever flows remains, whatever remains corrupts."

– John James

People with disordered eating often have a poor sense of boundaries. The reasons we do not set boundaries are many. Here are a few reasons that are based on fear. It is the fear of:

- Hurting someone

- Being abandoned

- Someone's reaction

- Being punished

- Being rejected

- Being shamed

- Someone's anger

- Seeming selfish

"But what torments of grief you've endured, from evils which never arrived."
- Ralph Waldo Emerson

In this chapter, we will discuss how our boundaries have affected our lives. Our boundaries around food are pretty obvious, but this is the effect, not the cause, of our problem.

The Building of Boundaries

Our problems can begin at a very early age. Boundaries may be violated physically when we are too young to understand or stop the abuse. Victims of abuse often have poor boundaries because they learned early in life that others could invade their space and do whatever they wanted. If this is the case, we can make adjustments in our boundaries with the help of a therapist, clergy, or other resource.

We may have a parent who has no boundaries, and that is what we learn. We may have a parent whose whole focus is on us because they have no other outlet or interests. They begin living their life through us. Because we want to please our parent, we rely on their external validation and disregard our connection to ourselves. We become dependent on the parent or others to make our decisions. We do not develop internalized coping skills or learn from our mistakes.

On the other hand, we may rebel against our parents. We do the opposite of what our parent wanted us to do. Rebellion does not come from our internal, authentic Self. Because we are reacting, instead of choosing our response, we are being controlled by someone else. This type of reacting can be subconscious and can last a life time if not acknowledged.

This can be disastrous in either case. We are left to the whim of external factors, controlled by others. We may seek relief from our inability to function by turning to addictions. We have no internal guidance system.

A child needs to be able to feel safe and be able to say things like

No.

I don't like that.

That is wrong.

___ told me not to tell you...

___touched me...

I disagree.

I feel...

It is really hard to have boundaries when we are not in touch with ourselves. Boundaries are imaginary or real lines around our physical, emotional, or spiritual Self that denotes limits for us and others. *Imaginary* lines can include such statements as, *It's not ok for you to talk to me like that.* An example of a *real* line is, *You can shake my hand, but you cannot touch my body.*

Lack of Boundaries and Disordered Eating

Disordered eating behaviors are formed in these uncharted areas where we disconnect from our feelings, thoughts, or situations and focus on pleasing or succumbing to some other person. We are no longer aware of the inner guidance system that tells us *something is wrong; a boundary needs to be set here.* Because we have redirected our thoughts from the hurt or pain to our obsessive disordered eating or thinking, we are not even aware of what caused the hurt or pain. Most importantly, we do not learn how we can avoid this in the future. We need to be able to ask ourselves, *what can I have in place so that this does not happen again?*

Let me explain. Someone pressures you into going to a place where you feel very uncomfortable. Maybe the first boundary could have been to say, *no, I don't want to go there.* But because we are not connected to Self, we don't even ask our Self that question. We want to be liked and accepted, and we know the other person would like us to go, so we say *yes.* Already, we start to feel uncomfortable. We start to think about getting something to eat or asking *how am I going to stick to my diet?* instead of dealing with the real feelings at hand. Then we beat ourselves up for coming to the event instead of recognizing the steps we could have taken to prevent this feeling in the first place. We go to the buffet or we think about the ice cream we will have when we get home. Our whole thought process then is about how fat we are or what a failure we are. The obsessive thoughts of food, weight, or body image prevent us from learning about our Self and the corrective actions we can take in the future.

By learning about our own feelings, likes, and dislikes, we can set reasonable boundaries. Do you see how a lack of boundaries can contribute to disordered eating? It's hard to get through the pain of life, but when we bury our feelings with our food distractions, we never learn how to take care of ourselves. We need to know our Self in order to set appropriate boundaries. For instance, if you know a food is a trigger, or if it doesn't make you feel good, you can choose not to eat it. If someone offers you one of these foods, you can say *no thank you*! If you are not aware of how the food affects you, or are afraid of hurting someone's feelings, you may disregard an important boundary. This is true self-care because we know how different foods affect us and we choose accordingly.

Boundaries Create Honesty

Does our "No" really mean "No"?

Low self–esteem and the need for acceptance prevent us from speaking our truth. The first thought may be to please someone else. This can make it hard to say *no*. We want to be loved and accepted. *No* feels confrontational. Actually, saying no builds trust. The person receiving a no also knows that your yes really means yes. If we are always saying yes, the people in our lives don't really know us, our boundaries, or our real truths. After awhile, we even fool ourselves. Lying, even to ourselves, erodes our self-esteem. Sometimes, we don't even know our own truth because we are so used to automatically saying yes. We may say yes just because we know that is what someone wants to hear. But is this being honest? Over time, people cannot trust our yes to really mean yes or our no to really mean no.

Truth makes us feel good about ourselves.

You can learn to be true to Self. You can learn to trust your feelings! Becoming more aware of your feelings and the consequences of your actions can help you create boundaries for the future. You create a better sense of Self. You gain respect because you are true to yourself and others. Boundaries help to establish your real truths. It is Self care. The better you get at setting appropriate boundaries, the easier life becomes. This is another freedom.

Over-Committing

Many of us use over-committing to avoid looking at our own Self. We have no time to look inward. We are not aware we are doing this. We may find a false sense of satisfaction in taking on other people's tasks or trying to control situations. Our sense of worth can get so caught up in giving that we don't realize that our own duties, feelings, and responsibilities are being neglected.

Often, other people are not grateful that we have taken over their responsibilities. They may feel inadequate or controlled by our desire to help. We may find ourselves feeling very tired, frustrated, drained, unappreciated, and unloved.

When we over-commit ourselves or try to control situations, it takes away our energy. We may turn to disordered eating to ease this stress and frustration. When we think we have to do something in order to be loved, we can never do enough.

Taking care of Self actually gives us more energy. We are better able to be all we were meant to be. When we are fresh and rested, we can see our own behaviors more clearly. We can truly be there when needed. When we take care of our Self, we have the energy to really care for others. Create a sense of your own space and time. Then you can better evaluate your priorities and discern where your help is really needed. Everyone benefits.

Boundaries help us distinguish what we need to take care of and what is not our responsibility. We may take on other people's tasks, maybe because they asked, but more often it becomes a distraction from looking at our own Self. We turn to disordered eating to ease the added stress or our inability to do everything perfect.

Setting Appropriate Boundaries

How can we set appropriate boundaries? Of course we have to start by connecting back to our Self. We need to be aware of our feelings and the consequences in our lives so we can choose more effectively in the future. Rather than turning to our disordered eating, we need to sit with the pain in order to learn more about ourselves and our actions. One important step is to know your own beliefs and values. We addressed this extensively in Chapter 6. Coming from your own beliefs and values, you can better guard this important, personal aspect of Self. We can learn to value this part of Self above the approval of others.

Another boundary to be aware of is our thoughts. Where is our mind throughout the day? It seems that we can't always pick the first thought that comes into our mind, but we can choose to change it and not dwell on it. This can be an important step toward healthy self-esteem and lessens our need to people-please. What do we allow into our senses? Have you noticed how some movies or music uplifts you and others bring you down? By knowing this about yourself, you can balance these external stimuli.

Overstepping Boundaries

When we are so obsessed with ourselves, we may forget to consider other people's wants and needs. Many people vacillate between being untrue to themselves and not thinking of others. Has someone ever said you were controlling, headstrong, or demanding? This could be because you are intent on getting your way without consideration for others. Here are some examples of overstepping boundaries.

- Opening a closed door without knocking
- Borrowing something from someone without asking
- Inviting yourself along
- Being late
- Assuming just about anything
- Staying longer when there are visible signs that the visit or conversation is over
- Expecting others to pay your way

- Setting appointments without consent from the other person involved

- Doing something for someone without checking to make sure its ok

The last item in the list could be a chapter in itself. We may be trying to help them, but it is possible that they interpret it as you not believing that they can do it themselves or that you doubt their abilities.

My Experience

I love my little sister. When we were growing up, it had been necessary for me to take on the role of a mother to her. But as we grew up, I found that I was giving her things or doing things for her that she never asked for. I loved her so much. I just wanted to make her life easier. Needless to say, this put a lot of friction on our relationship. Finally, it got to the point where we could not talk to each other without getting angry.

I learned that the things that I was doing for her were interpreted by her as *I don't think you are capable of doing this yourself, so I'll do it for you.* It seemed like I was always on a different level than her. You cannot have a healthy, loving relationship with another person when one person is better than the other – or at least when your actions show that. I was taking away her confidence and self-esteem without ever knowing it. I would step in and fix anything that went wrong in her life. I was stunting her growth. I was playing God to her so she never had to get her own relationship with a Higher Power. When this came to light, things began to change.

It was the hardest letting go I have ever experienced. It hurt from a place I didn't know I had. At first, we grew more distant because this old way was the only way we knew to relate to each other. A few months later, we came back together as peers. This new love for each other is so much deeper than before.

I got to watch her bloom. I became amazed at all the things she started accomplishing in her life. I saw her spirituality in action. She became whole. I wish I could have known earlier what I was doing, but it was not possible because I confused care-taking with love. We now encourage each other on our own paths. This love is so much more than what we had before. It was worth the pain of *letting go* to get here. I wish the same love for you.

Carl Jung's Remarks

Carl Jung provides a good reflection at this point:

"Your role as a helper is not to DO things for the person you are helping, but to BE things, not to try to train and change their actions, but to train and change your responses. As you replace negatives to positives, fear to faith; contempt for what they do to respect for the potential within; rejection to acceptance, not trying to make them fit your standard or image, or expecting that they need to measure up or down from that standard, regardless of what you think the best may be; dominance to encouragement, panic to serenity, false hope to real hope, self-centered to God-centered, the rebellion of despair to the energy of personal revolution; driving to guidance, self-justification to self-understanding – as you change in such ways as these, you change the world about you and all the people in your world for the better.

Self-pity blocks effective action. The more we indulge in it the more we feel that the answer to problems is a change in others or the world; not a change in us. Thus, we become a hopeless case.

Exhaustion is the result when we use energy in mulling over the past with regret, or in trying to figure ways to escape a future that hasn't yet happened. Likewise, setting up an image of the future and anxiously hovering over it for fear that it will or won't come true uses all our energy and leaves us unable to live today. Yet living this day is the only way to have a life.

Take no thought for the future of others. Neither expect them to be better or worse as time goes on, for in such expectations you are really trying to create. This is God's job, not yours. When man tries to create another life he makes only monsters. God alone can create. Love and let be.

Remember, people are always changing. When we judge what we believe we know of them, failing to realize that there is much we do not know, and that they are constantly changing as they try for better or for worse to cope with life. Give others credit even as all of us struggle; give them credit for having had many victories which are unknown. (We are all of the same cloth, though of a different cut.)

Remember, you too, are always changing and you can direct that change consciously if you so desire. Yourself, you CAN change. Others You Can Only LOVE.

If I am willing to stand aside and let God's will be done; I free myself from personal anxiety and a mistaken sense of responsibility." — Carl Jung

CHAPTER EXERCISE: Investigating Boundaries

Where have you not set a boundary because you felt guilty?

When did you say "yes" when you needed to say "no"?

How is your life unmanageable because of your lack of boundaries?

Describe how your lack of boundaries has led to overeating?

How do others in your life set boundaries?

When have you let someone hurt you because you feared the consequences?

What are you going to do to set appropriate boundaries?

© 2009 Rebecca Cooper   www.dietsdontwork.org   800-711-6336

CHAPTER 8 *Self-Discovery and Healing*

That which the dream shows is the shadow of such wisdom as exists in man, even if during his waking state he may know nothing about it... We do not know it because we are fooling away our time with outward and perishing things, and are asleep in regard to that which is real within ourself.
- Philipus Aureolus Paracelsus

How to Know

Journaling is a way to start getting connected to our Self. We journal by listening to our own thoughts and feelings. This forces us to go inside. Journaling is a way that we can start to become acquainted with our thoughts and feelings. As we practice journaling, the acquaintance becomes more than an acquaintance. We start to understand and know who we are. We start to identify our feelings and the events associated with certain feelings both past and present. We start to understand our mysterious Self. Through our connecting to our Self, we start to see what is missing in our life. We can then entertain ideas of what will fill the void we are feeling. We can learn to live in harmony with our inner Self.

Journaling can get you through some of the buried pain so you can heal and connect with the real you.

A page in a journal is a mirror of our inner Self. Thus, journaling is a tool through which we can get to know ourselves. This can be especially helpful if we are using food to push our feelings down. If we *just* start to become aware of the feelings, we can begin to make other choices besides using food to numb ourselves. A bonus is we can also get to identify the feelings that have been holding us back from achieving our goals.

The Healing Power of Journaling

In addition to helping us recognize feelings, the words we journal possess a healing power. Studies have shown that as we become more aware of our underlying feelings through writing, they can be healed in the process.

A 10-year study conducted by James Pennebaker, PhD. conducted on the effects of journaling states: "The act of writing can be an avenue to that interior place where free of pain and doubt, we can confront [emotions] and put them to rest – and heal both body and mind."

Further, the students who volunteered for the study support the findings. One student wrote: "Although I have not talked with anyone about what I wrote, I was finally able to deal with it and work through the pain instead of trying to block it out. Now it doesn't hurt to think about it."

Thus, writing is a step toward healing our thought process. Writing or journaling allows us to confront upsetting past events, thereby freeing us from them. The final summary states: "Indeed, the vast majority of our volunteers report feeling a heightened sense of relief, happiness, and contentment."

So, in addition to identifying feelings, a purpose of this type of writing is to help you resolve issues in your mind. Therefore, you might write about something that is *eating at you*. Just let the thoughts flow onto the paper. Even if the writing doesn't make complete sense, you may find a resolution to your conflicts that works uniquely for you. Then you no longer will have the need to block these issues with food or anything else.

A client commented about her experience with journaling; "At first I felt more depressed and cried while I wrote about what had happened and how I felt. I had been blocking that feeling out with food. That feeling never had the same hold it had over me in the past."

My Journaling Experience

One of the greatest obstacles I had in my early recovery was the fear of being abandoned. I had gone through extensive therapy concerning my childhood experiences with abandonment, but it was still there. I would pick relationships with men who were emotionally unavailable. Jack was there physically, but the emotional bond was conditional. If I did or said anything wrong he would totally blow up. He would tell me that I had to be out of his house in three days. We had been together for many years. I had quit working. I had no place to go and no one to help me. He wouldn't talk to me. Passing in the halls was unbearable. He would give me a look of disgust and pass without a word. This would go on for days. Then everything would be okay again. My life was on a chaotic rollercoaster controlled by my fear of abandonment.

Each time this happened I started journaling. I still have the tear stained pages. It was a bleak time. I would start out writing about the current argument and the associated feelings. Then my pen would take me to the associated feelings from the past. I wrote "this feels just like the time my mother left when I was six years old." I didn't know what was going to happen next. I didn't know where my sister and I would live or who would take care of us. The same theme came up about Dad dying a year and a half earlier. This feeling felt the same as when Grandpa died and especially when my grandmother died when I was sixteen. I cried and cried, not only about what was happening now in the present, but also about all those other times I felt this way.

With time, my overwhelming reaction settled down. I was no longer controlled by my past. I could look at what was happening now and I was free to make changes.

The Journaling Process

"Journaling breaks apart and breaks through the shells of our habits, which are the heavy baggage most of us carry from the past."
-Ira Progoff, PhD.

This is how journaling works to uncover issues and help you to connect to Self. An incident, thought, or feeling surfaces. In the past, you may have reached for, obsessed about, or restricted food so you wouldn't experience certain thoughts or feelings. When you journal, you write the thoughts and feelings down. You can't keep writing the same thing, so you go a little deeper, past the current issues. *You allow yourself to feel.* This directs you on to other unhealed feelings. You may become aware that this pattern or feeling has occurred in your life before. If you can touch on the pain, just for a minute, it heals a little bit.

Over time, journaling can get you through some of the accumulated pain so you can better connect with *the real you.* As you peel away the blocked pain and heal, you can experience "connectiveness." You'll feel more alive and begin to know who you truly are. You'll understand the saying "to thine own self be true" in a new way. You will be free of the hold this core issue had over you. You can find peace, joy, love, and happiness when you break through to connect with your true Self. It is not only the core feeling that we label as bad that gets suppressed. As we suppress this bad feeling, we also block our connection with other feelings. The accumulated blocked pain limits our ability to access all the other parts of our Self, including our appetite.

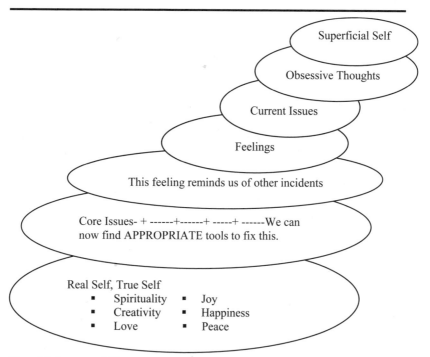

Figure 8.1: Journey to Self

So relax and don't think about it – just write it.

Here are some examples of different process types for journaling.

Process 1: Automatic Writing

Begin with a phrase or question such as "I don't know what I am feeling" or "Why is writing in my journal important today?" Then just let the words flow. When journaling, it is important to keep in mind that this is *just for you.* Don't worry about using correct grammar or sentence structure. Don't be a critic. Write one full page. Pay particular attention to the last paragraph. Sometimes surprising things will surface at the end of the page.

Example: What do I need to know today?

Why is writing or journaling so important? It connects me to my higher Self. Most of the day I hear my negative self-talk. When I write I have to look inward to find the things to write. I have to connect to my insides, my higher Self or spiritual Self. When I am connected to Self I feel more connected to God. I experience and am aware of more synchronicity around me. I feel life flows and not much upsets me because my core is calm. I intuitively know what I should do next. It may not be the results I think I want. Just stay connected to Self and be aware of the doors God opens. As I go through, open and look for the next step. Have faith not fear. There is nothing to fear but fear itself. Fear is what blocks me from the sunlight of the spirit. Just be still and know that I am loved, protected, cared for and guided. Then give thanks to stay on that positive side of Self.

Process *2*: Writing Yourself a Letter

What if your older, wiser Self, Higher Power, or God wrote you a letter? What would the letter say to you?

Dear _____,

Quit trying so hard. Let me show you what can happen in your life when you let go and follow my will. I know the best way. Trust me. I have a different perspective. I have been around for a long time. If you were 80 years old, what would you tell yourself today? There is wisdom of the ages and beyond yourself. Tap into me and let me guide you, show you. You are wasting time trying to figure it out. Your mind is so focused on trying to figure it out that you are missing my direction, my guidance through your quiet mind. Your mind is not quiet, so how can you discern my will in that muddy torment of whirlwind activity. Get still, calm and centered and watch for the miracles. Look for the signs, be fixed on that. You have so much good work that you can do. First take care of your spiritual health. Take care of your physical body so your mind and body can function together to the fullest potential. Be an example of what happens when you let God take over. Stay clear and focus on me. Put me first and all these things and more will be given to you. Thank you for your time with me. I love you and I have great things in store for you. Let me do the work and you can enjoy the ride. Life was not meant to be a struggle. If you focus on me first, life is easy, fun, and fulfilling.

Love,

Your Self

Process 3: Write a letter to someone from the past or present

Dear _____,

I have always wanted to tell you the truth about what really happened. I kept so many secrets then. I even hid the way I ate from you. You never knew the turmoil I was going through because I never let you in. There was no way you could have loved me because I wouldn't let you see the real me. I didn't know myself, much less love myself. I said I left because of you not communicating. But how could you communicate with someone who wasn't there? I wish I could have been different. I hope you found the love that you deserve.

CHAPTER EXERCISE: One Page Journaling

It is hard to get started journaling sometimes, so start with this one page. Notice what surfaces at the end.

I don't know what to write……..

©Rebecca Cooper 1999   www.dietsdontwork.org   800-711-6336

CHAPTER 9

The Blessing of Self-Esteem

This underlying perception of who we are expresses itself extensively in our lives.

Deep changes come as we begin to take the focus off dieting. We remove ourselves from the overeating patterns that caused us to create distance from our emotions and our Self in the past because we now have room to consider what could provide *true fulfillment* in our life. To stay on this path and remain committed to our growth, we must allow ourselves to try new things and sometimes make mistakes. Healthy self-esteem comes from walking through your fears. High self-esteem comes from our mastery and competence in different areas of our lives. Take the self-esteem test at http://www.dietsdontwork.org/selfesteem to

Love your neighbor as yourself.
Matthew 22:39 KJV

see where you are now. Change requires effort, perseverance, and commitment.

One of my clients, Janet, demonstrated how her beliefs about herself led her to disordered eating and isolation. Janet was brought up in a culture where she was criticized if she thought good of herself. She was told she was being conceited. When Janet put her needs before someone else, she was told she was selfish. She learned early that it was most important that others thought highly of you. At all costs, she must not do anything to bring disrespect to the family. She walked on eggshells. She put on a pretty face. She wore a smile continuously. She looked good on the outside.

As Janet grew older, she had problems with relationships. She criticized herself extensively. She tried to be self-forgetting and good, but all her relationships ended. She could not understand why.

Janet hated herself. Sometimes that anger came out onto other people. She hated herself when that happened. She turned to food. It became her closest companion. She spent more and more time eating. She thought about food all the time. Her life became very small and she was isolated.

Self-esteem stems from our beliefs and attitudes about ourselves.

As she became heavier, she no longer attempted to have other relationships. Her Self hatred and criticizing internal dialogue forced her into isolation. She felt so bad about herself that it was too hard to put on a happy face and be with other people. When Janet finally called me, she had gained 100 pounds. She said she could not come in for an appointment because she had not shopped for clothes in the last year. She said the only thing she could fit into was a food stained smock. After many phone conversations, I convinced her that I didn't care about how she looked or what she wore. Her condition was a matter of life and death. She finally went to her medical doctor and we began the long journey back to her Self and recovery.

Self-esteem is a blessing that you can give to yourself.

Self-Esteem Explained

Self-esteem equates to how we feel we can handle situations in our lives. It stems from our beliefs and attitudes about ourselves. Self-esteem includes what we think, feel, and say about ourselves, as well as those things we say *to* ourselves. This underlying perception of who we are expresses itself extensively in our lives.

It's important not to confuse self-esteem with selfishness. Conversely, self-obsession is not the way to increase our self-esteem. We can think of ourselves all the time and still suffer from low self-esteem. Therefore, it's not *how often* we think about ourselves, but rather the *quality of our thoughts* in regard to our self that matters.

Self-esteem is not boastful pride, conceit, vanity, or egotism. Healthy self-esteem is a byproduct of feeling we are capable, trustworthy, loving, caring, honest, likeable, etc. It is the ratio of our genuine accomplishments to our pretenses. The more aligned we are to our True Self, the more self-esteem we will have.

When we are emotionally healthy and have high self-esteem, we know our capabilities and equate our value in those particular areas. Let's say that you're an artist who paints, but you're not a mathematician. Doing poorly on a math test would not have the same impact on your self-esteem as not painting a picture.

So how does someone obtain healthy self-esteem? Well, if lack of self-esteem is an issue for you, it's quite possible that you have focused so much on your body size, diet, food, and your faults that you got stuck. However, here's the good news... *the cycle of low self-esteem can be broken!*

One solution lies in performing *esteemable acts.* Performing deeds that make us feel better about our Self brings about changes in our thinking. In other words, *right actions will lead to right thinking.* In time, this practice changes our thoughts and beliefs about ourselves and will improve our self-esteem.

On this note, consider how your conscious and subconscious beliefs about yourself can affect your actions.

- Have you ever thought about doing something, but never got started because your internal dialogue caused you to doubt your capability?

- Have you ever thought about saying something, but didn't because you concentrated on your inadequacies to deliver the message?

- Have you had an internal desire to let someone special know your true feelings, but kept the feelings inside for fear of rejection?

- Have you not let someone near and dear to you know the real you because you were afraid they might not accept you?

Think about other ways low self-esteem might negatively affect our behavior.

Self-Validation

How many people really love themselves? Looking at our world today, we have domestic violence, child and elder abuse, homicides, suicides, and war. I believe not loving ourselves is why the world is in trouble. People love others exactly the way they love themselves. Loving ourselves has been a message through the ages. It is so important for our Self and for others. If your self-esteem is low, you feel unworthy. You will not let love in from others and you have none to give from inside.

As you now know, when our self-esteem is low and unhealthy, it can manifest itself in many ways. Perhaps we will start looking for validation elsewhere. We may find unhealthy ways to feel better.

Some common forms of self-validation can be seen in the way people approach relationships or work situations. For instance, some people with low self-esteem wind up on the extreme high-end of the achievement spectrum. As overachievers, they channel their energies into attempts to receive recognition, approval, and affirmation. They become highly successful in their careers and educational endeavors; they are driven. They may become workaholics in their attempts to increase their sense of self-worth. They are frequently obsessive about completing projects, constantly striving for perfection or continually taking on huge new undertakings.

In other cases, low self-esteem can have the opposite effect and hold people back. As underachievers, they may not attempt to try anything new. They are afraid of failing, so they never start the project. Then they think about all the other projects they never completed. This becomes a self-fulfilling prophecy.

Underachievers who think poorly of themselves will tend to slink back in fear, never realizing their skills or talents. In their insecurity, they are frightened by the challenges they face and are vulnerable to the possibility of failure and humiliation. While these people are often capable and bright, they do not recognize or utilize their skills because their motivation has been so repressed and their fear of failure is so great.

On the other hand, with low self-esteem, we may hide our perceived inadequacies by practicing various numbing behaviors like eating or focusing on others.

Sometimes those with low self-esteem become rescuers of other people. They do this, not from a place of love, but with the intent to create the sense of worthiness and adequacy they feel missing from their own lives. This is almost always subconscious. They are not aware of their motives. Genuine acts of love and kindness are grounded in *giving*. These acts differ from those geared toward *receiving* favor. Be aware that healthy love requires a healthy self-esteem.

Random Acts of Kindness

When was the last time you performed a random act of kindness? How did you feel afterwards? Did you need to tell others about your kindness? Chances are, your recollection is a joyous one. It naturally follows that as we shower our goodness on others, we experience positive inward feelings, thoughts, attitudes, and beliefs about who we are. As our own goodness flows through us, it leaves behind the residue of internal joy, thereby increasing our self-esteem.

In order to obtain the full benefit of this practice, perform these acts of kindness without letting the recipient of your kindness know it was you. By diverting the focus from yourself, you are able to notice how you feel when you give selflessly, without expectation of acknowledgement or reciprocation.

Esteemable Habits

Habits are not what we are, but what we do.

Another key point in understanding self-esteem deals with recognizing that habits are not what we *are*, but what we *do*. As we repeat certain behaviors, those behaviors develop into habits. Therefore, we must ask ourselves, *which of our actions do we want to become habits?* It stands to reason that we have an important choice in determining which direction our behavioral patterns will follow. If we begin with esteemable thoughts, then take esteemable actions, we will feel our self-esteem heal and grow healthier.

If we begin with esteemable thoughts, then take esteemable actions, we will feel our self-esteem heal and grow healthier.

Remember, this process will not happen overnight. It requires practice. So be patient with yourself and understand that by taking small steps, you will eventually move along the right path.

Remember too that all journeys begin with a single step or thought. Today we can choose the direction we want to go. Once we take that first step toward our goal, the momentum will carry us forward. If you instead weigh yourself down with the thoughts of the past or the future, you won't experience the freedom of *the now.*

Remember also that a problem can't be solved at the same level at which it was created. Expand your mind and think outside the box. We've learned that food or obsessive thinking about dieting does not increase our self-esteem. Start using the tools that work, easily, effectively, and naturally.

Reinforcing Self-Esteem with Affirmations

Our subconscious mind forms the patterns for our thinking. Throughout the day, notice the evidence of your core thinking. Does your thinking support your goals in life? Does your thinking make attaining your goals harder? What would you say to encourage someone else? Frame it as an affirmation. Is it possible to use this affirmation at least once a day? Start noticing the times you can repeat this affirmation, not the times you didn't. Remember what you focus on gets bigger. Look at what you are focusing on throughout the day. Do you want more of that?

Practicing affirmations can help us to create healthy, positive self-talk.

Practicing affirmations can help us to create healthy, positive self-talk. When practiced for a sustained length of time, these affirmations take hold in our subconscious. Then, the new thinking and new beliefs can contribute to a healthier level of self-esteem in our core being.

This chapter includes sample affirmations that you can choose from as you begin. At some point, you may then want to create your own affirmations. In general, it's helpful to remember two important rules:

1. Affirmations need to be in the present tense, not in the future. The future tense always put you in a state of waiting and wanting. An example would be *I will achieve my ideal weight*. When will you? A better way of stating this could be *I am achieving my goal weight*. You want to celebrate you NOW!

2. The affirmations must be something that you find believable. You want these statements to expand and grow in your mind and life. Affirming that you are at your ideal weight when you are not is not going to register. The affirmation must be believable to you now.

One way to practice affirmations is through the use of flashcards. Select affirmations you want to be a part of your thought process. Write these down on index cards with one affirmation per card. Refer to these cards throughout the day.

Wisdom is avoiding all thoughts that are not in concert with your goals.

The most powerful way to practice affirmations is in front of a mirror. Surprisingly, this can be harder than we think; mostly because we are looking in a mirror to check what is wrong with our hair, face, etc. As a result, we are not used to saying or thinking encouraging loving thoughts in front of a mirror.

Therefore, this is often an excellent place to start. Take your cards to the mirror, read your statements to yourself, and then look into your eyes and tell yourself, out loud, your affirmation.

Then think of yourself as recycling any negative thoughts into positive ones. Visualize/imagine it – create the picture. Your subconscious mind is the computer.

Use affirmations daily. It's a very simple process, really. Wisdom is avoiding all thoughts that are not in concert with your goals.

Affirmations

Find affirmations that you would like to use from the list below, or use the list to inspire the writing of your own affirmations.

- I am letting go of the need to eat for emotional reasons.
- I am enjoying healthy choices more and more.
- I am free of compulsive eating at this moment.
- More and more, I can let go of self-consciousness and involve myself in the moment.
- I am getting better and better every day.
- I am human and I learn from my mistakes.
- I am taking better care of myself each day.
- More and more, I am learning to be true to myself.
- Each new behavior is the beginning of a healthy habit.
- More and more, I realize my body is my oldest companion.

- I appreciate my body and I am grateful for all it allows me to do.

- The better I take care of my emotions, the better life works.

- In my mind's eye, I see myself healthy, strong and fit, doing what I want to do.

- More and more, I can see my own strength and courage.

- I know that my growth is a continuous process and I am enjoying the journey.

- I can see that I am more confident now.

- I am more trusting of myself.

- I understand that I already have everything I need.

- I see myself surrounded by the energy of love.

- As I relax into the flow of life, my life works better.

- There is always enough! There is always more than enough.

- I allow others to take responsibility for their lives.

- I enjoy taking care of my body and hearing its needs.

- As I exercise, I feel confident knowing that I am giving my body what it desires.

- Healthy nutrition allows my body to maximize its potential.

- I can enjoy resting and relaxing.

- I am grateful for my sense of humor that reminds me that I am human.

- I am open to taking risks that will help me grow in positive, healthy ways.

- I value my emotions as a cherished part of my guidance system.

- My intuition is a barometer telling me what I need.

- I am beginning to accept, understand, and love myself more and more each day.

- I choose to keep my relationships healthy, open, and honest.

- I enjoy the adventure of my day.

Positive thoughts coupled with positive actions create predictable positive self-esteem and growth. Sometimes we need to work more in one area of our life than another. Some of the most impacting areas of low self-esteem are success, relationships, and work. Below are some thoughts to embrace in these areas.

10 Keys to Maintaining Healthy Self-Esteem

- Do esteemable acts.

- Practicing self-acceptance allows yourself to make mistakes.

- Set achievable goals. Know your capabilities.

- Change the way you talk to yourself. Use affirmations to reprogram your subconscious.

- Be yourself and tell your truth. Live in integrity.

- Make a list of your strengths and read it to yourself regularly.

- Practice Self responsibility. Praise yourself for what you have achieved.

- Review you strengths whenever you are feeling particularly defeated.

- Live purposefully.

Self-Esteem Test

This test is scored on the website. Answer TRUE or FALSE (honestly!) to each of these questions:

	T	F
1. I am usually comfortable with myself and others.	☐	☐
2. I feel as smart as my friends & co-workers.	☐	☐
3. I can usually get whatever I set my mind on.	☐	☐
4. What happens to me is usually in my control.	☐	☐
5. I am mostly competent.	☐	☐
6. I rarely worry about how things will work out.	☐	☐
7. I feel I can deal with most situations.	☐	☐
8. I feel confident in my ability to solve problems.	☐	☐
9. I don't feel guilty for asking others for help.	☐	☐
10. I usually take criticism as a point to consider.	☐	☐
11. Even when I fail, I know I am worthy.	☐	☐
12. I am mostly optimistic about my future.	☐	☐
13. I usually will speak my truth.	☐	☐
14. I feel that I have a lot of marketable skills.	☐	☐
15. I can politely disagree.	☐	☐
Totals	—	—

You can find your evaluation at

www.dietsdontwork.org/selfesteem

CHAPTER EXERCISE- Installing Affirmations

Write each of your chosen affirmations here. Stand in front of a mirror and repeat the affirmations while looking directly into your eyes. Notice the emotions that come up. Repeat going through the affirmations two more times. Then repeat this exercise each day for 2 weeks and start noticing how the affirmations start coming to your mind subconsciously.

1.

2.

3.

4.

5.

6.

7.

©2009 Rebecca Cooper www.dietsdontwork.org 800-711-6336

CHAPTER 10 *Overcoming Emotional Eating*

"All sorrows are less with bread."

Cervantes in Don Quixote

Biology isn't the only reason we eat. Food is powerfully connected to our emotions. For many people, the mere thought of a favorite food evokes strong associations that blend image, senses, emotions, and memory into a mixture that is nearly impossible to separate into the different parts. This is exactly the trap that many people who attempt to change their eating habits easily fall into. In other words, when you've just had your heart broken, green beans and baked fish aren't going to cut it if ice cream has been the soother and comforter of the past.

A Vicious Cycle

The more we try to ignore a feeling, the stronger it grows. It's so much easier to deal with an issue while the emotion is still in a *fixable* stage. However, our denial system is incredibly effective in shielding us from facing ourselves honestly.

Denial stems from a fear of admitting, "Yes, this bothers me." The consequences of this admission are even scarier!

Denial stems from a fear of admitting, *Yes, this bothers me.* The consequences of this admission are even scarier! Now we think, *I must take responsibility for making changes to correct the situation.* But admitting honestly to ourselves, *Yes, this is the emotion underneath my food craving* is such a tremendous relief! When we identify the emotion, we can find tools to deal with that feeling. That emotional relief then reduces, or even eliminates, the impulse to overeat.

If the food you crave is associated more with pleasure and immediate gratification than it is with pain, it's going to be hard to stop using it. So now the question has to be *How does that short-term pleasure stack up against the long-term pain and guilt of eating food that keeps you in pain?*

The urge to reach for food for emotional relief or self-soothing begins with our thinking. Our internal dialogue may emotionally stress us with any of the following thoughts:

If they only knew!	I always fail.	I am *so* fat!
I look terrible.	I can't do it.	I'm crazy.
She/he is better than me.	Who am I fooling?	I'm ugly.
No one understands me.	People are looking at me!	I can't get out of this.
What's wrong with me?!	I'll never finish.	I'm a failure!

As a result of our negative internal dialogue, our resulting emotions may be any of the following:

Helpless	Excessive worry	Lonely
Depressed	Irritable	Fearful
Loss of control	Impending doom	Panic

Trapped	Angry	Embarrassed
Uneasy	Rejected	Isolated

So how do we break the vicious cycle? First, we need to be *aware* of the emotionally upsetting thoughts. Then, we can learn to avoid the provoking thoughts and replace them with beneficial ones.

When you have the urge to soothe yourself with food, become aware of the messages you're telling yourself. Are they anxiety-producing or reassuring? You can curb your tendency to eat for emotional comfort by stopping the internal criticism and learning how to comfort yourself.

There are a few characteristics that set us up for increased emotional stress eating. They are perfectionism, being rigid or controlling, people-pleasing, and low self-esteem.

Perfectionism is one of these characteristics. Check any question to which you would answer yes:

- ☐ Do you criticize yourself when you're not perfect?
- ☐ Do you feel a constant pressure to achieve?
- ☐ Do you feel that you haven't done enough no matter how hard you try?
- ☐ Do you give up pleasure in order to be the best in everything you do?

Having an excessive need for control is another characteristic that sets us up for emotional distress. Do any of the following apply to you? Check the box for yes.

- ☐ Do you have to be perfectly in control at all times?
- ☐ Do you feel you need to plan everything?
- ☐ Do you feel that any lack of control is a sign of weakness or failure?
- ☐ Are you uncomfortable delegating projects to others?

People-pleasing is another emotional trap. Consider your responses to these questions:

□ Does your self-esteem depend on everyone else's opinion of you?

□ Do you sometimes avoid assignments because you're afraid of disappointing your boss?

□ Are you better at caring for others than caring for yourself?

□ Do you keep most negative feelings inside to avoid displeasing others?

Lack of self-esteem may be creating a feeling of *not being good enough*. Review the following questions to see if this may be an issue for you:

□ Do you feel you can never do as good a job as other people?

□ Do you feel your judgment is poor?

□ Do you feel you lack common sense?

□ Do you feel like an imposter when told your work is good?

The above-mentioned characteristics are roadblocks to living life to the fullest. Challenge these beliefs. Experiment by acting in a way that is opposite to your usual behavior. Evaluate the results for yourself. Replace these patterns of thinking with less emotionally upsetting thoughts and the need to eat to reduce your stress will decrease.

Ways to Reduce Stress

Simple modifications in posture, habits, thoughts, and behavior often go a long way toward creating a more relaxed way of living. Here are eight quick and simple things you can do immediately to help keep your emotions more in balance.

- **Delegate, Delegate, Delegate.** If you feel overburdened because of a need to control, delegate a task, and observe the consequences. It's likely that you'll see that others *can* accept part of the workload.

- **Control your anger:** Watch for the next circumstance in which you find yourself becoming annoyed or angry at something trivial or unimportant, then practice *letting go.* Make a conscious choice not to become angry or upset. Do not allow yourself to waste thought and energy where it isn't deserved.

- **Breathe:** Breathe slowly and deeply. Before reacting to the next situation, take three deep breaths and release them slowly. This actually fools the body into thinking you are relaxed. The mind will follow.

- **Slow down:** Whenever you feel overwhelmed, practice slowing down. Walk and drive slower. You'll find that you think more clearly and react more reasonably to situations. Stressed people tend to speak fast and breathlessly. By slowing down your speech, you'll also appear less anxious and more in control of any situation.

- **Complete one simple task at a time:** Choose one simple thing that you've been putting off (for example, returning a phone call or making a doctor's appointment), and do it immediately. Just taking care of one nagging responsibility can be energizing, improve your attitude, and get your momentum going.

- **Change your location:** Go outdoors for a brief break. Breathe in the healing power of fresh air. Don't be deterred by bad weather or a full schedule. Even five minutes on a balcony can be rejuvenating.

- **Avoid hunger and dehydration.** Drink plenty of water and eat small, nutritious snacks. Hunger and dehydration, even before you're aware of them, can provoke aggressiveness and exacerbate feelings of anxiety.

- **Avoid caffeine:** Coffee and caffeinated drinks pick you up fast, but also make you more irritated and anxious.

- **Do a quick posture check:** Look at how you are standing or sitting. Hold your head and shoulders upright and avoid stooping or slumping. Bad posture can lead to muscle tension, pain, and depressed feelings.

- **Recharge at the day's end.** Plan something rewarding for the end of a stressful day, even if only a relaxing bath or a half hour with a good book. Put aside work, housekeeping, or family concerns for a brief period before bedtime and allow yourself to fully relax. Don't spend this time planning tomorrow's schedule or doing chores you didn't get around to during the day. Remember that you need time to recharge and energize yourself – you'll be much better prepared to face tomorrow.

An Increased Need for Food as Fuel?

Our bodies were made to alert us to the need for increased fuel when we are under stress. What if our thoughts are telling our body that we need a large amount of fuel to supply us with the energy to deal with excessive amounts of fear, anxiety, and stress? We may mistakenly eat large amounts to have the energy to deal with this overload. But what if it is only our thoughts and there is no situation to deal with? When such a challenge is not dealt with in a manner that burns the energy, we can gain weight. This is especially true if the fear, anxiety, or stress is only in our thinking. Wouldn't it make sense to work on decreasing the levels of fear, anxiety, and stress in our life? This will reduce the messages that we need more food to cope with our feelings. So it follows that one of the ways of helping ourselves out of the emotional eating cycle is to decrease the false need for more energy from more food. Incorporating the above tools can help. Also, note that food cravings can have a physical root. See "Food Addictions," in <u>Diets Don't Work$^®$; Beyond Dieting</u> for more information.

Additional Solutions

"Let go" and "go with the flow." Spirituality and the belief that there is a greater goodness to help us in this life is a solution. It's hard to let go of our fears into a vacuum. It's easier to turn those fears over to a Higher Power or to God (however we define God).

We can also simplify our life. When we have too much going on, it creates a chaos in its own right. We can get clear about our priorities and what is really important in our life. Will the current activity really make a difference or lead us to our goal in five years, or could the time be better spent living *in the now*?

Changing Your Thinking

One way to reduce the emotional pressure in your life is to actively turn away from negative, tension-building thoughts and to consciously concentrate on positive, reassuring statements.

The urge to reach for food for emo-tional relief or self-soothing begins with our thinking.

Combating negative thoughts and replacing them with positive ones takes practice, but the results are worth it. Remember the acronym of FEAR: *False Evidence Appearing Real*. I have also heard it is the acronym for *Face Everything And Recover.*

Review the facts. What's your evidence? Is there another way to view the situation? If not, what is the worst thing that could happen? You may have been concentrating on the worst possible outcome, which by no means is the most likely one. What steps can you take to create a better outcome?

Here are some examples of pressure-building thoughts:

Pressured Thinking: *I'll never lose this weight*!

Alternative: *If I take it one step at a time, I'll make steady progress.*

Pressured Thinking: *My supervisor didn't say 'good morning.' He's probably displeased with my work, and I'll probably get fired soon*!

Alternative: *I'm jumping to conclusions. My supervisor may have been in a bad mood. Unless I get some negative feedback, I'll assume I'm doing fine.*

Pressured Thinking: *I can't get my mistake out of my mind. I am so stupid*!

Alternative: *I'm human, no one is perfect. I did my best, and I learned from my mistakes.*

Review the ideas for creating more supportive thinking in Chapter 5, "Change Your Thinking, Change Your Life."

Relaxation

Relaxation techniques allow you to have a better viewpoint to appraise situations accurately. Intense emotions can cloud your judgment and push you to reach for food as relief. Relaxation helps you to consider other thoughts and maintain a sense of self-control.

Focused breathing is an easy and effective way to calm yourself down. You can do it anywhere in any situation.

Deep breathing helps your body relax. It buys you time before you react, and it allows you to gain self-control instead of turning to food.

Below are a few tips for better breathing:

- **Become an observer of your breathing.** This will distract you from your thoughts about the situation. At the same time, you can determine your stress level by noting the speed of your breathing.

- **Breathe all the way down into your abdomen.** You'll know your breathing is deep enough if your belly starts to inflate.

- **Breathe out completely.** Squeeze out as much air as you can as you exhale. This will increase the amount of air that you inhale.

- **Practice deep breathing regularly.** Turn some of your daily breaks into deep breathing sessions.

"For fast acting relief, try slowing down."
Lily Tomlin

Therapeutic Counting is another effective and easy tool to use. Pay attention to your breathing and count with each breath from 1 to 10. When you breathe slowly, the body interprets the situation as calm.

Listening to calm music can take your mind and body to a more relaxed state.

Use guided imagery and meditation. The effect of daily practice brings long-term effects. Meditation will be covered in depth in my next book: Diets Don't Work®: Beyond Dieting.

In summary, there are many methods available to help you relax. With practice, a self-relaxation technique can drop you into relaxation any time you wish. The more you use it, the more effective it becomes.

Strategies to Curb Emotional Eating

Sometimes emotional eating is a sudden intake of a lot of food. In other cases, it's a mindless, less frantic consumption of food that fills up time. In either case, it can help to have strategies in mind to reduce the non-hungry eating you're doing.

- Journal during the evening hours when your temptation for emotional eating may become strong.

- Make helpful new rules to deal with your stress points, such as *no eating in the car*.

- Remove the *temptations* (usual foods) from your house.

- Practice mindful eating.

- Think it through. Ask yourself, *How will I feel after eating all this?*

- Tell yourself to *slow down*.

- Leave the environment that's tempting you to overeat.

- Call a friend.

- Allow yourself to cry.

- Relax, close your eyes, and picture yourself in a grassy wild field or at a beautiful beach.

- Turn on mellow music.

- Write about the positive changes you've already made.

- Tell yourself to wait 10 minutes first. Most times, the urge to do non-hungry eating will pass.

- Get busy with some project immediately after eating a normal meal.

- Have a cup of tea as a signal that the meal is over.

- Do something good for yourself: buy a book, take a bubble bath, shop, see a movie, or take a walk.

- Pray or write a gratitude list.

- Before preparing a meal, picture yourself mentally going into your kitchen and eating a healthy meal, then cleaning up and walking out of the kitchen. Visual imagery is very effective.

- Get out of yourself and do something nice for someone else!

Food Triggers

One of the best ways to know our trigger situations is to note them as they are happening. For instance, maybe one of your triggers is being alone at night, after dinner, or with nothing to do.

It is helpful to have a list of three alternative actions for each trigger situation ahead of time. It is hard to come up with an alternative action in the middle of a triggering thought, emotion, or event. Then at least you'll have a choice. Even knowing you have a choice is empowering. Even if you do react the same old way, you are learning more about your trigger. If you can be open to this learning process, you can change. It's only when we retreat into the habitual criticizing of ourselves or overeating that we lose the opportunity to learn about our Self, others, and grow.

Diet's Don't Work®

CHAPTER EXERCISE-Food Triggers

A. You can change only those things of which you are aware. **Awareness is the first step.** List your top 5 food triggering situations:

1.

2.

3.

4.

5.

B. Now review the list of strategies in this chapter. Start to match up strategies with your five trigger situations. Then add some alternatives and coping ideas of your own.

Trigger #1

Trigger #2

Trigger #3

Trigger #4

Trigger #5

©2009 Rebecca Cooper www.dietsdontwork.org 800-711-6336

CHAPTER 11 *Coping in New Ways*

"If the only tool you have is a hammer,
you tend to see every problem as a nail."
Abraham Maslow

If the only tool you have is eating, you tend to see every problem as a problem that dieting or losing weight will solve. We need to find new tools. This requires change.

Change can be scary. It's like jumping off a cliff, not knowing where, how, or when you will land. This state of limbo is most unsettling because it's the opposite of the control we're trying to achieve through dieting and stuffing our feelings with food. It seems we'll do anything to try to maintain some sense of control in some part of our life. But the questions we need to ask ourselves are *What really needs my attention?* and *Am I focusing my energies on what's actually important?"*

It is not what we have on the outside that will make us happy. It is that peace on the inside that we were looking for all along.

Loss of Control

We start with a diet to control our weight until we vary from the appointed plan. When we vary from the plan, we feel out of control. We have been using the food plan to control our eating or not eating. To get back into control, we go back on another diet or divert our attention to something else to control. The more bizarre and limiting the diet is, the better it seems to work. This is because having a plan gives us a better sense of control. We know exactly what we should or should not eat.

We feel good about our Self if we are in control. It can also be scary because if we are in control, we are responsible; we are the manager of our own fate. But then we wonder if we have all the right information to lead us into the happiest, calmest, most fulfilling life. This self-doubt sets up fear and insecurity. One of the ways we are accustomed to handling fear and insecurity is to try harder - redouble our efforts. The stress becomes greater as our sense of Self becomes buried behind thoughts of working harder. In time, we become consumed by the stress, free-floating anxiety, and impending doom. We either burn out, melt down, become psychotic, get sick, end relationships, create more chaos, isolate from the world, or change.

We have an innate desire to be free.

But how do we progress from control to change?

Most of us realize that we need to grab onto something that is permanent, secure, safe, and powerful enough to get us through a transition. Sometimes we use other people, but after a while we rebel. We have an innate desire to be free.

Sometimes we use drugs or other things to help us be in control, but this too fails in time. Then the substance can control us instead of us being in control.

Sometimes we use work, church, activity, success, prison, gurus, etc. to keep us in control. But eventually we rebel, so we search for another avenue of control.

So what can we latch onto in a healthy way during the process of changing? In my decades of experience in helping people who have an obsession with dieting and emotional eating, the most successful approach I've seen is an inward directed, one of connecting to Self and your own spirituality. Much of the work in this book is about reconnecting to Self. The next chapter will focus on this in more depth.

The key to change is to be willing and open. Once we become willing and open, we will see our path unfold in the most amazing ways. We practice honoring our intuition and feelings. We learn that some things seem right to us and others do not fit. We learn that we don't have to reject the whole concept if there are parts we feel uncomfortable with. We learn a little here from this source and a little there from another person, book, idea, or experience. We may find that we grow faster around like-minded people, so seek out these teachers. This is not giving them the control; this is fueling the potential of your True Self. It's like taking the Real You to a playground. Enjoy the journey; embrace the changes, knowing that you are heading toward a new way of life that is filled with self-love, respect, peace, and happiness within yourself.

The key to change is to be willing and open. Once we become willing and open, we will see our path unfold in the most amazing ways.

When we worry and try to control situations, people, or things, it saps our energy. We become more worried and more controlling until we are spinning out of control. It is then that we realize that when we let go, a natural flow takes over. We can now make use of all that wasted energy and become centered and empowered.

I've had a lot of problems in my time; fortunately most of them never happened."
Mark Twain

Facing Our Feelings

The remainder of this chapter will largely look at dealing with some of our most challenging feelings... *anxiety, anger, fear, hurt, loneliness, etc.* Once we look at an underlying emotion, we no longer need to stuff it down. Life becomes easier and we react emotionally to *present* situations and deal with our feelings *currently.*

Anxiety

Even the thought of anxiety can make us anxious. What is this emotion, and how can we put it to good use instead of being victimized by it?

Physically, anxiety is like fear. The main difference is that when we are afraid, we usually know what we are afraid of. When we are anxious, however, we often don't know the root cause of the feeling. Anxiety is a vague emotion. We might notice sweaty palms or a racing heartbeat, or we might find ourselves playing out situations in our minds over and over again. Sometimes, because of our anxiety, we purposely avoid certain situations or activities that really should be part of our life. We let our anxiety rule our behavior and, in doing so, miss out on so much that is enriching and wonderful!

When we feel anxious, we send a danger signal to our body that is intended to help us avoid harm. This can be very handy if we are outrunning a saber-tooth tiger, but is not very helpful when we're trying to get some sleep, communicate with a spouse, or communicate with a colleague. Note that in a small percentage of cases, symptoms of anxiety may stem from a medical disorder that can be successfully treated.

The vast majority of anxiety symptoms are the result of negative predictions of the future. That prediction usually involves two general beliefs:

1. Something bad is going to happen, and

2. We won't be able to do anything about it.

What are most people anxious about? Research has shown that there are two primary areas of concern:

Fears about physical health

Fears about negative social consequences

When a patient discusses these issues with a cognitive therapist, they explore the risks the patient perceives. By talking about fears in a safe, confidential setting, many people are able to quickly recognize the thoughts that are causing their anxiety. Cognitive therapists use a process called *guided discovery*, which allows patients to identify thought patterns that trigger discomfort. Thoughts (such as fear) drive feelings (such as anxiety), which in turn drive behaviors (eating when you are not hungry). So if you can catch those negative thoughts as soon as they occur and change them to be positive thoughts, you can, in fact, change the feelings and the behaviors as well.

Benefiting from Anxiety

How can we make anxiety work for us?

We can start by understanding the meaning of our body's signals to us. Rather than a catastrophic interpretation of our sweaty palms or racing heart, we can understand that our body is trying to get our attention.

Instead of automatically assuming that there is real danger, we can instead ask ourselves, *What thoughts or images are going through my mind*? One question many people find helpful is *What's the worst that can happen*? Frequently, this will help us to become more aware of the thoughts that are frightening us.

Once we're aware of the worst possibilities, we now can consider the *upside* or the positive possibilities. Asking ourselves, *What's the best that can happen*? can help us to become aware of other possibilities.

Asking ourselves, "What's the best that can happen?" can help us to become aware of what usually is the opposite extreme of our fears.

Take a moment to reflect on some of the things you have worried about, and see how they tended to turn out. You may find that many things have turned out better than you thought.

Having examined the extremes of what could possibly happen, we can turn our attention to the probable. Many people suffer needlessly simply because they confuse the possible with the probable. It's possible for our house to fall down but, because we don't consider it probable, we dismiss that thought from our mind and feel comfortable about the issue. Asking ourselves, *What is most likely to happen*? can help us arrive at a prediction that is likely to be more accurate than either of the extremes we have identified.

Remember that the second negative prediction we make when we're anxious is that we won't be able to cope with the bad thing that we fear. To test the validity of this belief, we can ask ourselves the following question. *Even if the worst happens, what could I do to cope*? This can help us to update our awareness of resources for responding to problems. This is the time to get creative and come up with some possibilities you hadn't thought of earlier.

Finally, take or plan some action to influence the situation that you have identified as threatening. Rather than resorting to old ways of dealing with tension (such as staying stuck in it or eating for relief), ask yourself, *What are some steps I can take now, or soon, to influence the outcome of this situation*? Again, it's time to get creative. If you feel stuck, ask a friend to help you *brainstorm* possibilities.

If you make a conscious effort to catch your negative thoughts as they occur, work through them, and change them to positive thoughts. You will, in turn, reduce your anxiety. You will find yourself leading a much happier and rewarding life – and isn't that where we all want to be?

Some Facts about Anger and Eating

Some of us don't know what to do with anger. We may have grown up thinking it was not appropriate to get angry, or maybe we learned that anger could intimidate or keep other people away. Maybe we learned we could get our way with certain displays of anger. Maybe we felt a rush of power, or the extra adrenaline gave us more energy. Maybe we never got in touch with anger until it appeared as rage. Whatever our history, many of us pushed this uncomfortable feeling down with food.

To abandon oneself creates resentment and anger.

Now that we are getting in touch with our Self, we might be realizing that some of our anger can arise from not taking care of ourselves. To abandon oneself creates resentment and anger.

We may also be using anger to defend against feeling hurt. In these cases, we don't feel the hurt, but in time our anger causes us to push away relationships. Avoiding hurt causes us to withdraw. We are not able to acknowledge our human vulnerability.

Anger can also serve as a defense against feelings of loss. We build a wall to cover the loss. The short-term effect is that we don't feel sad. In the long-term, however, we never resolve the grief and can't bond with others. Anger helps us to avoid feelings of helplessness.

Anger creates a feeling of control. We feel in control by getting anger mobilized. It gives us energy and a sense of empowerment. Some of us use anger for the adrenaline rush. This can become addictive.

Anger can be used to cover up fear and to defend against low self-esteem. It is easier to feel anger than to feel fear, hurt, guilt, etc. The problem is in the aftermath. Anger leads us away from appropriate actions, leaves us with damaged relationships, and makes us feel bad about ourselves. Anger keeps us from dealing with the source of our fear. It prevents us from being able to explore other options.

We also can be angry with others instead of looking at ourselves. Anger keeps us from dealing with our own *self critic*, that is, how we talk to our Self. The use of anger shuts off the self-criticism, but we cannot change the way we talk to our Self if we are focusing on someone else.

Anger stunts our problem-solving skills and ultimately leaves us feeling helpless. By constantly using anger to turn away from the real problem, we fail to practice constructive action.

To properly cope with our underlying feelings, we must identify what feeling lies beneath the anger by asking ourselves, *If I wasn't angry about this situation, what would I be feeling?* Then we can deal with the underlying problem.

Anger not released unleashes depression and disease. Anger suppressed is expressed covertly.

Any person capable of angering you becomes your master; he can anger you only when you permit yourself to be disturbed by him.
- Epictetus

Anger not expressed is expressed covertly.

Tools for Dealing with Anger

- **Give yourself permission to express anger.** We are taught at an early age to hold in our emotions. This can have a profoundly negative effect on our overall health. It's not wrong to express anger, fear, and hurt. In fact, it is healthy to release these emotions regularly. It is preferable to find safe ways to release these negative feelings.

- **Combine mental and physical effort.** One of the most effective ways of releasing anger is to combine mental and physical effort. This is accomplished by doing a physical activity along with the mental intention of releasing the anger.

- **Never hurt others in the process of expressing anger.** Give yourself the opportunity to express anger in a safe way, without hurting anyone else. Some people prefer ripping pages of a newspaper, pounding pillows, screaming, throwing plates (old ones), etc. Remember, NEVER hurt yourself in the process, and never aim your anger literally at another person. What's important here is your expression of the negative emotion, not who receives it. Be open to discovering your own dynamic anger-release method.

Keeping a resentment makes you hurt, not them.

- **Strive to forgive**. The final step in maintaining anger-release is to truly forgive the person who wronged you as well as to truly forgive yourself. You do this for you, not the other person. Keeping a resentment makes <u>you</u> hurt, not them.

Is it really Fear?

The direst foe of courage is the fear itself, not the object of it, and the man who can overcome his own terror is a hero and more.
-George Macdonald

Fear is a common underlying emotion of anger. If we're not aware of our fears, we may go to great lengths to stay unaware. Here are some categories to use in examining possible stumbling blocks:

- **Fear of the unknown**, impending negative events, or lack of control in your life and especially fear of change.

- **Fear of bodily harm**, resulting in worry about automobile, plane, or other accidents; thoughts of pain, germs, and illness; or phobias of heights or enclosed spaces.

- **Fear of failure,** resulting in fretting about effectiveness on the job, thinking and acting defensively, being unnecessarily critical of others, hesitancy to undertake new projects, and quitting before an evaluation.

- **Fear of being unloved,** resulting in jealousy, possessiveness, feelings of rejection, insecurity, and thoughts of not being needed.

- **Fear of being ridiculed,** resulting in a tendency to be shy and quiet, hesitancy to express new personal ideas, fear of speaking before a group of people, or being easily embarrassed.

- **Special personal fears,** like the fear of being misunderstood, fear of being controlled or emotionally hurt, or fear of being inadequate sexually.

Is it really Hurt?

Feeling hurt can masquerade as anger. Acknowledge that you are hurting if this is your truth. Is the cause realistic or imagined? If realistic, be assertive by expressing that hurt to a safe person and consider the following.

Emotional pain is a lot like physical pain. Both tell us that something is wrong and in need of correction. Usually we can do one of two things (or sometimes do them in combination):

1. We need to act differently, and/or

2. We need to think differently.

Many times, we cannot change a situation. The only way to find peace is by acceptance. I'm not talking about acceptance of the unacceptable! Acceptance of the unacceptable creates a separation of Self. You may have been using food to avoid acknowledgement of this type of separation. You can now choose how to deal with unacceptable situations. What I mean by acceptance is to recognize that we cannot change the reality of a particular situation and, therefore, <u>must deal with it</u> as it is.

Other Considerations

Facing Unworthiness
Listen to your inner dialogue. Restate the thoughts accurately and specifically. Include a balance of realities and don't label yourself

simply for making a mistake. For more help, see Chapter 9, The Blessing of Self-Esteem.

Facing Grief

Acknowledge if anger is covering up the grief. Mourn your loss. Familiarize yourself with the stages of grief: denial, anger, bargaining, sadness, and acceptance. You'll find more info on grief in Diets Don't Work[®]: Beyond Dieting.

Facing Helplessness

We feel most helpless when we think someone else is causing our pain. Take your power back. If you focus on what can be changed (you), not what you can't change (them), then you can make changes.

The loneliest place to be is in the company of someone who is not there.

Facing Loneliness

Loneliness is never crueler than when it is felt in close proximity to someone who has ceased to communicate. The loneliest place to be is in the company of someone who is not there. Reach out when you feel lonely and do something for someone else. They may feel lonely too.

Simple Ways to Quiet a Noisy Mind

As I've pointed out, emotional upset is often triggered or accelerated by our thoughts. To turn down the provoking chatter in your head, take some of the following steps.

1. **Let go of suspicion and resentment.** Nursing a grudge is a major factor in unhappiness. A desire to *get even* can stir discontent twenty-four hours a day. Getting even is never possible; there will always be another potential resentment. It's really up to you to carry it or not.

Learn to live in the NOW.

2. **Give up living in the past.** This is an unhealthy preoccupation with old mistakes and failures. This feeds depression along with frustration and helpless anger.

3. **Don't spend too much time in the future.** If you live in the future, you will miss your present life.

4. **Give up wasting time and energy fighting conditions you cannot change.** Cooperate with life instead of trying to run it, run away from it, or force your future. Learn to live in the NOW. It can dramatically decrease your stress levels.

5. **Participate in the living, active world.** Refuse the temptation to withdraw and isolate during periods of emotional distress.

6. **Refuse to indulge in self-pity when bad things happens.** Accept the fact that nobody ever gets through life without sorrow and loss. Make it a growing experience.

7. **Don't ask too much of yourself.** Have reasonable self-expectations and don't set your goals too high. Feelings of inadequacy will result from not being able to accomplish unrealistic goals.

8. **Pray.** Finding a spirituality that works for you can help immensely.

9. **Meditate.** Learn to be still and relaxed. With practice, this can be a tool that centers and balances you.

10. **Be true to yourself.** When we live in alignment with our values and beliefs our minds stay calmer.

11. **Don't have your lights turned off and your mind turned on.** If you cannot go to sleep, read or get up instead of letting your mind be a party you would rather not attend.

Finding Happiness

Happiness is not achieved by having everything you want, but by wanting and being grateful for everything you already have.

We cannot find true happiness by seeking it in people, places, or things. When we try to find happiness through these, we become disillusioned. Another person cannot be responsible for our happiness. Eventually, they will let us down or flee from the burden of an impossible task.

Happiness is being grateful for what you already have.

Likewise, obtaining financial goals only produces additional responsibilities and concerns. Seeking pleasure just for us produces short-term happiness and a growing need to sustain the level of pleasure. So how do we find happiness?

The most devastating place to be is to have everything and still not be happy. Now, there is nothing else to achieve or get to make us happy. We are at a total loss. All the things we thought would make us happy, did not. Our life seems futile. What a waste of time and energy we have expended to find that we were chasing an illusion.

Some of us then see that it is not what we have on the outside that will make us happy. It is that peace on the inside that we were looking for all along. We start accepting life as it unfolds and see the miracles of living in the present on our life journey. The happiness we are looking for can only be found in the present.

Here are a few points to ponder:

- Make a decision to look at the glass half-full instead of half-empty. This habit, when cultivated, produces remarkable results!

- Happiness is a by-product of living a life full of meaning and purpose.

- Expressing gratitude for what we currently have in our lives seems to produce more of the same, just as constantly affirming the negative events in our life produces more problems.

Judgment comes from experience, and great judgment comes from bad experience. -Robert Packwood

- Share a part of yourself with another. Whether it be a material sharing, a spiritual one, or your time, the act of giving produces happiness for the giver as well as the receiver.

- Live life as best you can. Get in touch with your own values and be true to yourself. Everyone has an innate code that can lead to a life lived congruently with their inner most values.

- Realize you are human, and humans make mistakes. You can't move ahead if you are constantly focusing on your mistakes. Learn from them. They can be the most valuable lessons you'll ever learn.

Carl Jung had some wonderful thoughts on taking care of our emotional self. Examine some of the following excerpts to see what makes sense for your life.

"Self-pity blocks effective action. The more we indulge in it, the more we feel that the answer to problems is a change in others or the world, not a change in us. Thus, we become a hopeless case."

"Exhaustion is the result when we use energy in mulling over the past with regret, or in trying to figure ways to escape a future that hasn't yet happened. Likewise, setting up an image of the future and anxiously hovering over it for fear that it will or won't come true uses all our energy and leaves us unable to live today. Yet living this day is the only way to have a life."

"Take no thought for the future of others. Neither expect them to be better or worse as time goes on, for in such expectations you are really trying to create. This is God's job, not yours. When man tries to create another life, he makes only monsters. God alone can create. Love and let be."

"Remember, people are always changing. When we judge what we believe we know of them, we fail to realize that there is much we do not know, and that they are constantly changing as they try for better or for worse to cope with life. Give others credit even as all of us struggle; give them credit for having had many victories which are unknown (we are all of the same cloth, though of a different cut)."

Remember, you too are always changing and you can direct that change consciously if you so desire. You can change you!

Diets Don't Work®

CHAPTER EXERCISE- New Ways of Coping

What are some new ways to cope with and move through the following without using food?

	NEW COPING TOOL
Loss of Control	
Anxiety	
Anger (fear or hurt?)	
Fear	
Making a Mistake	
Moving through Grief	
Helplessness	
Loneliness	
Quieting your Mind	

© 2009 Rebecca Cooper

www.dietsdontwork.org

800-711-6336

CHAPTER 12 *Filling the Emptiness*

What we're feeling through this sense of emptiness at our very core is a need for a deeper connection.

In examining our experiences with compulsive overeating, many of us came to realize that we may have used food to fill the emptiness within ourselves. It feels like we have an empty hole inside us that does not fill. We feel alone and disconnected. Most of my clients tell me that the hardest time to control their eating is when they are alone with nothing to do. They are by themselves and they feel lonely. Being alone and being lonely can be two entirely different conditions. Being alone can be peaceful. Feeling lonely is anything but peaceful. Eventually, we found that this emptiness left us with a yearning that food, alone, could not satisfy.

We may have tried other methods to fill this need such as relationships, work, or even alcohol or drugs, but these only provided temporary relief. These substitutes took the focus off of the emptiness, but in time replaced it with self-loathing. At best, this repeated substitution merely served as a distraction from an inner urging toward fulfillment.

Basically, we are human beings in search of fulfillment. When we numb ourselves with food, we lose our connection with our internal Self that guides us toward our purpose in life. We feel hopeless and empty. Consequently, we become preoccupied with body size and our internal debates over what to eat or what not to eat to fill the void. We become focused on diet plans and how well we are doing or not doing, etc., but this just masks our inner emptiness. It never really fills it. So we beat ourselves up, all the while blaming our inability to control our eating for our emotional discomfort.

A Call from Within

The more we become willing to depend upon a Higher Power, the more independent we actually are...
Alcoholics Anonymous 12 Step & 12 Traditions

An inner emptiness can haunt anyone. Someone may have even succeeded in every area of their life only to find something was still missing. What we're feeling through this sense of emptiness at our very core is a need for a deeper connection. This fact seems to indicate that just as every other part of us has a need, our deepest part – our spiritual self – also demands nurturing and attention.

Spirituality is a very personal experience. Mind you, I'm not talking about external religion. Religion can be a vehicle to spirituality, but spirituality is something different. It is an internal connection with your Higher Power or God. Countless people have found many ways to express their own personal spirituality. For this purpose, I encourage you to fit this chapter's work into the framework of your individual experience.

Dependence

Some of us don't want to become dependent on a religion or God. We may not even believe in God, but recovery seems to happen faster to those who have some belief that there is a power greater than themselves that can help them change. Even if we do not understand it, we can see the effects.

We can gain strength – and help break unhealthy habits – by tapping into our own spiritual core. There are various spiritual practices designed to help us do just that. There are many avenues for exploring spirituality, including working with a clergy person, sponsor, or spiritual director, if that is your choice.

Have you noticed how some people seem to go through life with an inner calm and peace that doesn't match their external experience? These people, when questioned, will usually express a belief in God or a Higher Power. Their faith and peace are rooted in a spiritual life that is bigger than them or their situations. The way to this type of inner peace is through spiritual nurturing. Just like feeding their body with healthy food, these folks have fed their inner Self with spiritual fuel.

Many people have a variety of methods that seem to bring about this calm. Let's list some here in no particular order:

- Being in nature
- Living in the NOW
- Reading spiritual literature or the Bible
- Listening to music
- Looking at art
- Tapping into your own creativity
- Meditating or being still
- Being with like-minded people
- Praying
- Helping others
- Journaling
- Expressing gratitude
- Practicing forgiveness and acceptance
- Making restitution for mistakes
- Searching for higher motives than our own personal gain
- Looking for the miracles occurring in everyday life

"Each of us is empowered to drink from the cup of spirituality that quenches her own thirst."
Sue Patton Thoele

Through practice, we find that we no longer need substitutes to fill this spiritual void. Nothing short of our connection with our own spirituality is satisfying. We finally realize that food will never fill our spiritual emptiness. We then surrender and stop choosing the paths that lead to a dead-end and walk in the sunlight of the Spirit. We stay in the flow of goodness.

When one is a stranger to oneself then one is estranged from others too. - Anne Morrow Lindbergh

With an awareness of a God or Higher Power, we gain confidence knowing that we are not alone. We feel more connected. We can now handle life with this coping power. We enjoy a sense that really everything is all right. We recognize that we are not in complete control and we are relieved of the burden of feeling that we always have to make the right decision on our own. There is a newfound peace and calmness in knowing that life is just as it should be.

So now that we have cleared away the obstacles and distractions, let's begin the process of filling the inner void with substance, not temporary fixes.

Here are a few suggestions to help you get started. Try the ones that best suit you and your lifestyle.

Meditation: Sit comfortably, close your eyes, and relax your muscles. Breathe slowly and naturally. As you breathe, pay attention to your breath. Repeat a word, phrase, or prayer that calms you. If other thoughts come to mind, let them slide on by. Imagine you are at a train station. Watch the railroad cars go by. Start out for five minutes and build up to twenty minutes.

Prayer-walking: As you walk or jog, repeat a special word or short prayer every time your foot strikes the ground. Just repeat this in your mind as you move on down the road. Not only will negative internal dialogue drown out, but you will notice lightness to your heart and step.

Inner dialogue: Picture an imaginary place in a natural setting where you feel safe and nurtured. In this place of calm, ask your Self for an intuitive thought as you face various opportunities, life situations, and crises.

Spiritual Dependence

Think about the things we are dependent upon and use even though we don't understand how it works. Look at how this dependency helps you.

- Electricity
- Microwave
- Cell Phone
- Radio
- Computer
- Can see, hear
- Have air to breathe

Researching Spirituality's Effects

Scientists are now examining the healing effects of spirituality in laboratory settings and reporting amazing results.

For instance, in a randomized, double-blind study in Kansas City, Missouri, 990 consecutive patients were admitted to the Mid America Heart Institute over a twelve month period. They were sorted into two groups. One group received intercessory prayer (someone prayed for them). The other group did not (at least as part of the study; nobody can say whether friends and family were praying for them).

We can gain strength – and help break unhealthy habits – by tapping into our own spiritual core.

There were seventy-five intercessors who never met the patients. They were drawn from various denominations in the local community, but all agreed with the statement *I believe in God. I believe that He is personal and is concerned with individual lives. I further believe that He is responsive to prayers for healing made on behalf of the sick.*

The intercessors were asked to pray daily for twenty-eight days for *a speedy recovery with no complications*. None of the patients knew about the existence of the study.

To determine whether the prayers had any effect, the researchers looked at the patients' coronary care unit (CCU) scores. Since points are added to the score for each complication, lower scores indicate better outcomes. By this measure, the prayers appear to have been beneficial; members of the prayer group fared 11% better than those who weren't prayed for.

There's something that sets this study apart from others that show health benefits deriving from prayer. This one focuses on intercessory prayer for patients who did not even know they were receiving it. Many of the other well-publicized studies consider the effects of prayer, but the patients are aware of the prayers. The "placebo effect" could account for the increased wellness.

While the success of the latter may be ascribed to a variety of mind-body interactions (stress reduction, immune-system bolstering, etc.), the mechanism of intercessory prayer is inherently more mysterious and has proved more difficult to document. While an often-quoted study conducted at San Francisco General Hospital in the 1980s showed positive results from intercessory prayer, critics point out that those results have never been duplicated.

Until now.

This study was published in the October 25, 1999 issue of *The Archives of Internal Medicine* if you would like to explore it further.

As you enrich your spiritual life, it can empower you to achieve well-being in at least five different ways:

1. Fills the inner emptiness

2. Increases your sense of purpose and level of satisfaction with life

3. Provides a source of assurance and peace during times of stress

4. Makes you feel connected

5. Provides hope

CHAPTER EXERCISE -Expanding Your Spirituality

Write down some thoughts about what your spirituality looked like in the past, how it is today, and what steps you feel comfortable with to nurture this side of you.

1. Past Spirituality:

2. Present Spirituality:

3. Steps to Nurture My Spirituality:

© 2009 Rebecca Cooper www.dietsdontwork.org 800-711-6336

CHAPTER 13 *Assertiveness Matters*

By asserting our will, many a closed door will open before us.

Seyyed Nasr

Jewel wasn't sure why she had agreed to go to the horse races in Del Mar with her husband Jim. However, she knew even before they left the house that she didn't want to go. Maybe it was partly because they often ended up arguing about his gambling at the track, and partly that she was exhausted from a busy week at work. As they sat in the bleachers and watched the thoroughbreds round the course, she stuffed down her resentment with a steady stream of food. First, it was popcorn, then cotton candy, then pizza, and now she was biting into a candy bar. Little did she know that it didn't have to be this way… she could have asserted herself and simply stated that Jim was free to go, but that she wanted to stay home. Meanwhile, Jim was oblivious to his wife's inner struggle, and he grinned at her as the horse he was betting on began to gain a lead in the current race.

When we are assertive, we act in our own best interest, attempting to meet our own needs as well as the needs of others.

What Assertiveness Is and Isn't

When we are *assertive*, we stand up for ourselves, without abusing the rights of other people. We express honest feelings, letting others know our needs. We act in our own best interest, attempting to meet our own needs as well as the needs of others. We choose to respond to a given situation instead of reacting. We assume that *You are O.K.* and *So am I.*

In contrast, a *non-assertive* person, like Jewel in the example above, will have something she wants to say, but holds her honest feelings inside. In failing to express her true feelings, she is forced to wait for others to anticipate or guess about her needs and wants. She may allow others to control a given situation or even her life. She assumes *Everyone else is O.K.* and *I'm not O.K.*

Sometimes, people who don't understand assertiveness will confuse it with being aggressive. When we are *aggressive*, we stand up for ourselves, even if others are hurt in the process. An aggressive individual meets her own needs at any cost, expressing feelings bluntly. She tries to control every situation, often controlling the lives of others. She assumes *I am O.K.* and *Others are not.*

Let's look at some more characteristics of assertive, non-assertive, and aggressive people.

The *assertive* person achieves a balance between being passive and being aggressive:

- Is *direct.* Uses fluent, well-modulated voice tone.

- Inflection congruent with verbal message. Has good eye contact.

- Expresses opinions and feelings appropriately. Feels expressive and secure.

- All gestures and facial expressions are appropriate to verbal message. Listens.

- Relaxed mood. Self-enhancing and self-expressive.

- Respects the rights of others. Feels good about Self and other person.

- Chooses for Self. Is true to Self and others.

- Other person feels respected. Other person feels self-expressive and heard.

- Other person may achieve desired goal. Probable mutual understanding.

- Expresses feelings and takes responsibility for Self.

The *non-assertive* person tends to be:

- Indirect. Speech is hesitant. Speaks in low voice or tone.

- Has poor eye contact. Says what she thinks you want to hear.

- Nervous mannerisms. Listens, but is afraid to talk.

- Apologetic mood. Is self-denying.

- Lacks self-respect. Feels inhibited and anxious.

- Allows others to choose for her. Violates her own personal rights.

- Person feels guilty and angry. Others think poorly of the non-assertive person.

- Others achieve desired goal at the non-assertive person's expense. No mutual understanding.

- Does not express her feelings. Afraid to take personal responsibility.

The *aggressive* person may be:

- Indirect or direct. Has a harsh, demanding, loud voice tone.

- Looks at you with a penetrating, fierce stare. Uses *put downs* or demeaning statements.

- Uses threatening gestures. Doesn't listen, interrupts.

- Threatening with a hostile mood. Self-enhancing at expense of others.

- Feels superior and dominant. Chooses for others.

- Violates rights of others. Other person feels defensive, humiliated.

- Invades personal space of others.

- Others feel afraid of the aggressiveness. Others do not achieve own desired goals.

- No mutual understanding. Expresses feelings, but blames others for them.

Claim Your Assertive Rights

Assertion skills can be learned and sometimes they need to be re-learned because we've gotten out of practice. In any case, they are an important part of your ability to function and meet life's challenges. Include these assertive rights in your daily thinking and gain self-respect, as well as respect from others:

- I set my own priorities.

- I say *NO* without feeling guilty.

Do you express your needs, feelings, and opinions?

- I am competent.

- I am proud of my accomplishments.

- I feel and express my anger.

- I am treated as a capable human being.

- I make mistakes and I am responsible for them.

- I change unwanted situations.

- I can say, *I don't know.*

- I can be listened to and taken seriously.

- I can say, *I don't agree.*

- I can say, *I don't understand.*

- I express my needs.

- I express my opinions.

- I express my feelings.

- I can say, *I'm not willing to accept that responsibility.*

- I accept my imperfections.

- I ask for help when I need it.

- I am willing to grow, learn, and change.

- I recognize my needs as important.

- I can choose not to assert myself.

Can you say, "No, I'm not willing to accept that responsibility?"

Becoming More Assertive

Incorporating assertiveness skills into your life takes some effort at first. As motivation, realize that the more you assert yourself without being aggressive, the easier life becomes.

Here is a step-by-step process to becoming more assertive.

Step 1 Observe your own behavior. Are you asserting yourself adequately? Are you satisfied with your effectiveness in your interpersonal relationships? Look and see how you feel about yourself in different situations.

Step 2 Concentrate on a particular situation. Spend a few moments with your eyes closed, imagining how you handled one specific situation. Imagine vividly the actual details, including your specific feelings at the time and afterwards.

Step 3 Review your responses. Notice your strengths and the parts of the situation in which you were assertive, non-assertive, or aggressive.

Step 4 Consider alternative responses. What are other possible ways the incident could be handled? Could you deal with it more to your own advantage? Less offensively?

Step 5 Imagine yourself handling the situation in a new way. Close your eyes and visualize yourself dealing effectively with the situation. Be assertive, but be your natural Self.

Step 6 Try it out. Having examined your own behavior, considered alternatives, and imagined a model of more adaptive action, you are now prepared to begin trying out a new way of dealing with the problem situation.

Step 7 Shape your behavior. Repeat the assertive behavior to become more confident in dealing with the stressful situation.

A Look at Assertive Communication

We need to look at our real motives for having the upcoming conversation. Are our motives to manipulate, disempower, convince, discredit, put down, or anger the other person?

The purpose of assertive communication is to come to an understanding about a problem and maintain a positive, functional relationship. Inherent in this purpose is the process of negotiation for a mutually acceptable compromise.

Consequently, it is important to communicate what you are willing to compromise on and that you are actively seeking a mutually agreeable solution to the problem. In order to be satisfactory over a period of time, the compromise you are negotiating has to be workable for all parties concerned.

The use of "I" statements are a hallmark of an assertive person. It designates ownership of your judgments, perceptions, insights, and proposals. You clearly become the source and the ultimate judge of your communications and behaviors.

Using the *I statement* also allows you to let someone know how you feel about something without making the other person wrong. In short, you own your feelings and do not put the responsibility on other people. For example, you could say:

I am really frustrated with the way you talk to me" versus *You frustrate me.*

I feel left out when I am not included in a business meeting versus *You make me feel left out.*

A variation of the "I" statement is the *I want* statement. This technique supports you in communicating specifically and concretely what it is that you want or would like to see happen:

I would like you to let me know at least twenty-four hours in advance when you expect me to work late.

The next time we face this problem, I want you to level with me right off the bat and not withhold information.

The *I want* statement clarifies specifically what you want. You clarify for others what it is that you are willing to tolerate and what it is that you are unwilling to be subjected to on a regular basis.

Assertive communication requires:

1. Self-awareness - Know your Self.

2. Empathy - Put yourself in their shoes.

3. Listening - Don't rehearse what you will say next.

4. Authenticity - Be real.

5. Self-confidence - Believe in yourself.

6. Honesty - Tell your truth.

The purpose of assertive communication is to come to an understanding about a problem and maintain a positive, functional relationship.

The following are things that impede assertive communication:

1. Defensiveness - Feeling attacked.

2. Self-consciousness - Worried about what the other person thinks of you.

3. Competitiveness - Trying to surpass someone else's abilities instead of your own.

4. Preoccupation - Not really being present.

5. Passive-aggressive behavior - Acting out negatively later.

6. Impatience - Not letting the other person finish talking.

7. Power struggles - Trying to be in control.

Diet'sDon'tWork®

CHAPTER EXERCISE: Becoming More Assertive

Pick a situation that you were not comfortable with. Use the steps discussed in the chapter to become more assertive.

Step 1: What was your behavior? How did you feel about your reaction?

Step 2: Describe in detail how you handled the situation. How did you feel at the time and after?

Step 3: Where were you assertive, non-assertive, or aggressive?

Step 4: How could you handle the situation differently?

Step 5: Close your eyes and imagine handling the situation assertively.

Step 6: Practice Step 5 in real situations.

Step 7: Repeat until the new behavior becomes natural.

©2009 Rebecca Cooper www.dietsdontwork.org 800-711-6336

CHAPTER 14

Forgiveness Frees Us

How many times have you wished you could change someone else?

Use your energy where it will have results, with you.

A client named Nicole told me of a horrible event in her life. When she was thirteen, her home was broken into late one afternoon. The man tied up her mother and raped Nicole right in front of the mother. I was surprised to see this well-adjusted woman in front of me. She had been through such a trauma. As we talked, Nicole told me of her anger toward her mother. At first, I didn't understand this anger.

The client had received help from a therapist after the tragedy. With time, she was able to forgive the man for the sake of her own well-being. She now counsels rape survivors. Nicole was able to use that terrible tragedy in a way that gave meaning and purpose to her life.

Nicole said that the saddest part was not that she was raped that day, but that she lost her mother because of the incident. She told me that after that event, her mother became very angry. This anger turned into depression. Over time, the mother became more and more depressed and angry. She ended up being institutionalized. Nicole said that man ruined one day of her own life, but not her whole life. Her mother let him destroy her whole life and herself.

There are many reasons to forgive. It frees you from the negative emotional tie to another. Similar events don't trigger you into exaggerated emotions and reactions in the present. You can stay present instead of reverting to a painful event in your head or using food to push the awareness from your conscious.

What Is Forgiveness?

When you truly forgive, you do not forget, but remembering does not re-open the old wounds.

Forgiveness is mostly about you. It's not necessarily about the person you're forgiving. Forgiveness does not condone a wrong action. It does not absolve the other party of guilt or make them innocent. Forgiveness is not denial, rationalization, or repression of past events and feelings. When you truly forgive, you do not forget, but remembering does not reopen the old wounds. Forgiving does not instantly restore trust. Trust and feeling is rebuilt over time. Forgiveness is a gift you give yourself. *It is a choice.*

You need to forgive others because harboring resentments always hurts you. The other party may not even be aware of your emotional reaction. Resistance to forgiving creates more pain and hurt in our life than the original injustice because it occurs over and over again in our mind. Focusing on the wrong done to us sets many of us up to eat to suppress our feelings about the injustice. So another reason we forgive is because holding onto the negative emotions triggers our emotional eating. Resentments poison us.

Underlying Feelings

Note that forgiveness is not an emotion. The emotions behind the need to forgive often involve anger and resentment. Let's look at the differences between these two feelings.

Anger is a very normal and healthy emotion, and it is O.K. to feel angry at times. It tells you something is wrong. If we don't allow ourselves to feel anger, we may be missing out on very important cues for self-care. Sometimes we feel anger because we need to stand up for ourselves or change directions. Some of us beat ourselves up for feeling this perfectly appropriate emotion. Behind anger is usually one of two other emotions – hurt or fear.

The definition of the word resentment is *a feeling of indignant displeasure or persistent ill will*. Let's break down the root word from Latin. *Re* means *relating to, Sentir* means *to feel, to sense, or to suffer from*, and *Ment* means *again, and again, and again*.

When we are carrying resentments about the past, we're at the mercy of anything and anyone in our environment that will remind us of our pain.

Can we stay in the now and be experiencing resentment? I think you know the answer. By definition, resentment is usually about what has occurred in the past, yet we are experiencing the emotion again and again in the NOW. We miss what's going on in the moment because we're dwelling on the resentments of the past. We lose part of each day or hour that we spend ruminating about our resentments.

When we are carrying resentments about the past, we're at the mercy of anything and anyone in our environment that will remind us of our pain. We're always walking on an emotional mind field.

Sometimes we find that we're angry because someone has overstepped our boundaries. We stuff it down and try to forget it. We tell ourselves that we can just *let it go*. However, as time passes, *it* eats at us and we end up *eating at it*. Still, we may pride ourselves for not saying anything; it wasn't such a big deal, we think. Then we may find the feelings that we stuffed down manifesting in other behaviors, like indignation, a look, that tone, the silent treatment, or the cold shoulder. Keep in mind that over 65% of the American language is done through body language, 25% through intonation, and only 10% through words!

Perhaps we let things build up and then explode at minor incidents because of all the emotions bubbling under the surface. We may passive-aggressively attack others. We may have even *given them a piece of our mind*, and then ate over our guilt or remorse for our actions. In reality, we used these situations to continue our emotional eating patterns. It is crucial to be aware of the emotions when they occur and be able to state our truth in the moment so that it doesn't fester.

How to Heal Your Feelings

1.**Find someone to listen to you vent your anger as soon as you can when these feelings come up.** (Hint: Choose someone who is a good listener as opposed to someone who is looking to add fuel to the fire.) When we talk about the experience, we are able to process through the feelings, begin to see things from a more clear perspective, and then let it go.

2.**Write it all out.** Go through as much detail as you need and allow your emotions to fill the paper. You may wish to burn the writing in a personal ceremony later or keep it in a journal. You can seek professional assistance if you are finding it difficult to either access or release your anger, or you see a pattern of experiences and behaviors.

3.**Take a spiritual perspective**. I once questioned why a negative event happened to me. I was told, "Realize that some of the negative events happening can be your participation in someone else's life lessons. Maybe their interaction with you will bring them an important lesson. One part of Self helping another part of Self to become whole. We see ourself in others."

Figure 14.1: Heal Your Feelings

When someone says or does something, it can trigger unresolved emotions. This, in turn, can trigger emotional eating.

However, in order for us to achieve inner peace and comfort, we need to forgive. As you do this, the path becomes free and clear, and inner peace returns.

Being "Triggered"

In Chapter 10 on Emotional Eating, you looked at the typical situations that trigger your emotional eating. Let's look now at another type of trigger.

When someone says or does something, it can trigger unresolved emotions. This, in turn, can trigger emotional eating. When you become aware of the types of comments or behaviors that can trigger you, they will not have the same effect. As with your typical emotional eating situations, you can change your response with awareness of these triggers. It's when you own them that you can change.

How many times have you wished you could change someone else? Maybe you tried through manipulation or control. It takes a lot of energy to get someone else to change. Use the energy where it will have results-with you.

After an upsetting conversation or interaction, have you ever felt that you just wanted something to eat, even though you knew you were not physically hungry? This is your red flag. This can lead you into a new awareness, if you do not stuff it down. In that moment, the emotion that needs to be healed is right there. This is when you can touch it, acknowledge it, and heal it, a little at a time, until it is no longer a trigger to overeating.

"Madness needs not be all break-down. It also may be breakthrough. It is potential liberation and renewal as well as enslavement and existen-tial death."
R.D. Laing

What if you practiced a new reaction when that trigger came up? We know food or thoughts of food have not been a cure-all. What else might work? Just like we do with the situational triggers, prepare yourself by making a top three list of alternative actions for each conversational or behavioral trigger you can think of now.

We can change. We will have the energy to change if we focus that energy in the direction of growth, wellness, and acceptance.

When we are triggered with old emotions, we are being blessed with an opportunity to heal those wounds. I believe the universe will give us as many opportunities we need to be able to remem-ber and heal our own wounds. The only way to get to the other side of a feeling is through it. With each opportunity we can use it as a way to heal or to pile more pain on top of the original pain. You can choose to ignore the pain until it gets so great that you have to deal with it, often in the form of a substitute coping behavior gone awry. This substitute behavior now becomes the problem with the repressed events behind it. Food is often used to repress the emotions until food then becomes the problem. That is why using food can be so hard to give up. It's not the food, it is all the repressed emotions bottled up inside. When you start to

Use your own reactions as an indicator of wounds trying to surface to be healed. It is about unfinished business and unresolved emotions.

address food issues, sometimes this hidden layer seems so difficult that we revert back to overeating, etc.

If we allow the triggered pain to surface, just for a moment, we are on the road to recovery.

Changing Our Patterns

When we harbor grudges, we shut ourselves off from the positive qualities of our lives.

It's plain to see that resentment leads only to futility and unhappiness. When we go in that direction, we squander the hours that might have been worthwhile. When we harbor grudges, we shut ourselves off from the positive qualities in our life.

In order to live fully, we must release ourselves from our anger and resentment. *We do not avoid the feelings. We become <u>aware</u> of what we feel.* We look at the experience and see where we have given up our own power and given other people our power. We can see how the wrongdoings of others, fancied or real, actually dominated us. We cannot wish experiences away, avoid them, or *eat* them away. It's time to take <u>action</u>.

We realize that at times others may be *spiritually bankrupt*. And, while we do not like how they treat others, <u>compassion</u> is the key. If someone is physically ill, we do not normally get resentful at that person. We may need to show the people who stir our resentment the same tolerance and patience we do for someone recovering from a surgery or illness. How do we treat a sick friend or child?

Let's avoid retaliation or argument. Let's look instead to ourselves and for our response – our reaction to the behaviors of others. Even though a situation may not be initiated by us, we can look to ourselves to see what pattern we're following when we get resentful. Inevitably, we'll fall into an old response pattern when we get angry or upset with someone. Look to see if you either feel threatened or angry. See if you are fearful of what you will lose or fearful that you will not get what you want.

What we want to do now is develop the habit of identifying our emotions and owning the feelings. Then we can simply respond to the experience. Emotionally detaching from reacting allows us to be able to respond. It is not necessary to take things personally.

As we look at our behavior, we see that we have simply continued on with subconscious patterns set earlier in life. It is a freedom to be responsible for our behaviors. We always have a choice in how to respond or to react to our experiences. We can allow other people in our lives the dignity to do what they must as we allow ourselves to take care of ourselves. If we're in a place where we are being demeaned or degraded, then we need to take a look at why. We must uncover our *need* to place ourselves into a situation where we do not honor ourselves. This awareness and truth can put us on a road to recovery.

We always have a choice in how to respond or to react to our experiences.

Until we are willing to take a look at our patterns, we will find that, indeed, history does repeat itself. But as we grow, our perceptions change. We see the glass is half-full instead of half-empty.

Let's examine a sample resentment:

Example:

Resentful At:	The Reason:	Affects My:	Feelings:
My parent	Always telling me how to raise my children	Self-worth Self-confidence	Hurt, Anger, Frustration
Why Forgive?			
I will feel better now.	I have an ongoing relationship with my parents	It will free me from thinking about it all the time	To find peace

Figure 14.2: Why Forgive?

Sometimes looking at the cause of the resentment can shed new light on your choices in forgiving. When did this incident happen? How did you feel then? How do you feel today? Does it still affect you? Is it worth the wasted energy?

What else was going on at the time? What was your part in the disagreement? Did you allow yourself to express your true feelings? What could be the lesson for you to learn?

My Mother and Self-Forgiveness

When my mother, Ann, was twenty-four, my Dad was killed in a car wreck. Mom had no money and no way to care for her two young children. She left us with a babysitter, thinking at least we would be fed. She didn't come back, and eventually we were turned over to the state and then our paternal grandparents. We didn't see Mom again for thirty years. She had remarried, but felt at the time that she couldn't provide for her second husband's children and her own too. Ann ate at the feelings of guilt and hopelessness. She became morbidly obese.

Growing up, I stuffed the pain with food and an eating disorder. As an adult, I would try to find my mother. I would get a lead and then it would lead to nowhere. I carried that feeling that if my mother didn't love me I must be unlovable. I felt sorry for myself and angry at her. I used more and more things to try to push these feelings from my awareness. My life became hell on earth. I was alone with my eating disorder all day and all night. Then the miracle of recovery happened.

One day I was in a support meeting and I heard a young lady crying because she couldn't take care of her children. She couldn't even take care of herself. All of a sudden I got it. I saw my mother at 24 years old. I went up and hugged that young lady. I understood. I felt compassion. Shortly after that our congressman, Ron Packard, located my mother. After thirty years of separation, it was bittersweet. Mom could not connect to us on an emotional level. She had buried all that a long time ago. She was physically there as much as she could be, but found it too hard to look at us in the eyes. She could not forgive herself.

I remember a time when she came to visit my sister Rhonda and me. She spent hours playing computer games. I remember standing behind her, staring at her back, realizing I would never have the connection I had hoped for. She had shut down the pain, but also the joy that could have been. My mother died a few years later. She died of morbid obesity.

The Power of Self-Forgiveness

How can you forgive others without first forgiving yourself? Many of us try so hard to forgive others, but we don't look inside and clean out our own guilt, shame, resentments, and past hurts. We do this so the healing of forgiveness can enter into our own soul.

The hardest person to forgive can be our Self. It can take a lot of courage to feel the pain that was created by us, but it is the only way to clear away the barriers and walls so that we can really connect to another person. How can you give love if you don't have love for yourself inside?

We need to forgive ourselves. This will allow us to treat ourselves better. Once we clear out these old energies or patterns, we free up our energy to stay on track with our life's purpose and make room for life to assist us in manifesting our dreams.

Sometimes there's nothing better that you can do than to sit right down and write your Self a forgiveness letter.

Here's an example:

I'm sorry that I have been too busy for you. I know I've made promises in the past to take better care of you and then failed. I let other things become more important than you. It's so easy to let time with you slide away into the busyness of life. I want to nurture you and help you to become all you were meant to be. I know when I do this, I will have more to give others. When I give without taking care of myself, I become resentful because I am running on empty. Please be patient with me. I love you.

Diet's Don't Work®

CHAPTER EXERCISE-A Self-Forgiveness Letter

Now write a letter to yourself:

Dear Self,

© 2009 Rebecca Cooper www.dietsdontwork.org 800-711-6336

CHAPTER 15

Living Diet Free!

"I never resist temptation, because I have found that things that are bad for me do not tempt me."

George Bernard Shaw

As we focus more on healthy eating behaviors, we naturally start eating normally. Have you noticed that anything you focus on gets bigger? *How do people eat normal*? is a question I repeatedly hear. So let's start this chapter by taking a look at how people who are naturally slender look at food. By studying them and finding out how they do it, it's possible for us to learn how to stay at an optimal weight in a normal and healthy way.

Natural Eating

People who are naturally slender don't feel forced to be thin. They don't feel bad about *missing out on good food*, and they don't restrict their diet. On the other hand, dieters do all those things, plus some of the following:

- weigh themselves constantly
- major topics of conversations are about dieting

- compare themselves with others

- eat what they don't like

- always looking for the diet that will really work

- don't eat when they are hungry

"The curious paradox is that when I accept myself just as I am, then I can change."
Carl Rogers

Rather than waging a constant battle with food, it's much easier to learn to think and respond the way naturally slender people do. You can have the same mindset and habits. I wish I had known this earlier in my life. I thought a diet was the way to control my weight. After years of non-dieting, I have maintained my ideal weight without trying to. It took some time for my metabolism to stabilize after years of abuse. At first I gained 17 pounds in 3 months. I was horrified, but I was so sick of being sick and tired all the time and was willing to go through the temporary water retention and weight gain. I remember looking at myself in a mirror. I saw my thighs and tummy were bigger. I started to cry. Then I looked into my yes and said, *"I'm doing the best I can right now,"* and accepted where I was and was ok with me. I was happy to be off the yo-yo dieting rollercoaster and disordered eating. It may sound strange, but that extra weight came off without me trying or hardly noticing. I would have three meals a day. I would eat when I was hungry and stop when I was full. For me, I didn't eat between meals because of my propensity to binge. If I felt like I wanted something between meals, I would make sure to include that food in my next meal. Sometimes I would have potato chips with my dinner.

In retrospect, I now know that the reason for that initial weight gain was because I was learning to be aware of my appetite. I had lost the ability to know when I was full and when I was really hungry.

Here is how I do it. First, something makes me think of food. This might be seeing that it's time for lunch, hearing someone mention lunch, feeling hunger, or seeing food. I check my appetite to determine my next step. If I am hungry, I ask myself, *What am I in the mood for?*

I eat the food that would make me feel best – over time. Sometimes a food that seems like a good idea initially may not be good for me in the long run.

You may be wondering, *But what keeps you from eating chocolate, ice cream, and other fattening things!?* The answer is *Nothing*. Occasionally, I do eat fattening things, usually in normal portions. Absolutely nothing keeps me from eating fattening foods. However, I usually don't want to because I've realized that most fattening things make me feel worse over time if I eat them. If I imagine eating an entire basket of greasy onion rings and imagine feeling them in my stomach, slowly digesting them through the afternoon, I get a heavy, *yucky* feeling that is not appealing. If I imagine eating a big bowl of ice cream, it gives me a similarly unappealing, tired, depressed, and dull feeling.

Of course, each of us will respond differently to different kinds of food. You may find that for you, a turkey sandwich or a shrimp salad are what make you feel good and sustains your energy level. Remember that what makes you feel good one day will be different than what makes you feel good another day because your body changes over time as you respond to events: what you ate yesterday, your activities, how much sleep you got recently, how hot or cold you are, etc. Any food will probably be much more appealing if you haven't just eaten it three days in a row.

Another difference between naturally slender people and dieters is in what they do when they overeat, gorging on some kind of fattening food. Yes, everyone overeats sometimes. But when dieters overeat, they often think to themselves, *See, I knew I couldn't do it. I guess I'm just a glutton. I'm doomed to be overweight for life, so I may as well get used to it. Since I can't stick to diets anyway, I might as well eat and enjoy food.* A strong feeling of depression or worthlessness often keeps this pattern going.

Remembering the Goal

What we are looking for is having more good feelings – more pleasure rather than more remorse, depression, and physical complications. You no longer need to use *shoulds* and *rules* to try to force yourself to eat in ways that will make you lose weight. This program teaches you to think about what food will give you the best feelings over a period of time. Overeating may be pleasurable in the moment. However, by imagining how one would feel afterwards is not very appealing. A different choice can be made. Think of the bloating, the remorse, the weight gain, the depression, and being so tired afterwards. Is it worth it for two minutes of numbness?

This works even if you don't know the calorie count of a food item. If you've had an experience of overeating before, your body remembers your response to it. This creates an automatic inner motivation to eat well – because overall it's more pleasurable to eat this way. By actually going ahead and overeating on that food, and noticing how my body felt, I got a compelling experience of discomfort that I thought of the next time I considered overeating that food. We all learn from experience. Anytime you're wrong in your guess, you can be glad you had that experience so you can become more accurate in the future.

For various reasons, some individuals – those with food allergies, food addictions, or physical conditions like diabetes – require a restricted diet. You already know the harmful effects some foods will have on you. This eating strategy will still work well. If a person has an allergy or addiction to sugar, for example, and that person imagines how they will feel over time if they eat sugar; especially the sugar rush, then the drop of blood sugar levels, being tired and sleepy, feeling depressed and then craving more will be a reminder. This strategy can actually help those with allergies or sensitivities avoid inappropriate foods without internal conflict. It is a choice.

The same strategy allows you to decide when to stop eating. Each time you're about to take a bite, you can very quickly sense how that bite will feel in your stomach over time. It is important to be eating consciously. This means eating slowly, tasting the food, and checking in with your appetite. Of course, you stop as soon as you feel satiated because the next bite would make you feel less comfortable than you are now. This gives you a natural way to stop when you're full. As this process becomes a habit, it happens naturally and without your having to think about it. Your appetite now is in charge.

Note: Some people have a rule about eating everything on their plate. Many people eat everything on their plate *so it won't go to waste*, but it does go to waist! If you have this rule, you may want to take smaller portions, so you can be comfortable going back for more until you've had just the right amount.

I once told a client to imagine the sound the garbage disposal makes when she is tempted to clean her plate. Ask yourself, *Am I using my body as a garbage disposal right now*? This client said that every time she thought of going past her full point, just to finish the food, she would hear the sound of the garbage disposal and stop.

Breakfast – Don't Skip It!

The majority of people (80-85 percent) with weight problems skip breakfast on the rationale that if they don't eat, they will lose weight. This is a falsehood. In actuality, breakfast is the most important meal of the day! Our sugar level has dropped to its all time low after sleep. Our body has usually gone a minimum of eight to ten hours without food, and while the body is physically resting, it is using up the nutrients to keep the body in perfect functioning order. We need a consistent source of food (fuel) for the body. Restricting breakfast is a sure way to gain weight! Breakfast starts the metabolism for the day. People who skip breakfast burn 5 percent fewer calories every single day!

Diet's Don't Work®

CHAPTER EXERCISE: What I am Willing to Do

Check all the items you are willing to do:

- ☐ Stay off the scale.
- ☐ Start the day with reading spiritual readings.
- ☐ Do yoga.
- ☐ Eat slowly and mindfully.
- ☐ Meditate.
- ☐ Enroll in therapy: group and/or individual sessions.
- ☐ Attend self-improvement classes, support groups or plan activities in the early evening hours when the temptation to overeat is greatest.
- ☐ Change old behaviors by making new personal rules, such as "no eating in the car."
- ☐ Remove the binge foods from your house, office, and car.
- ☐ Eat without reading, working, watching television, or being on the computer.
- ☐ Eat breakfast every day.
- ☐ Ask yourself, "What's the 'pay off' for overeating this time?"
- ☐ Think about how you will feel after overeating.
- ☐ Slow down.
- ☐ Leave the environment that's tempting you to binge.
- ☐ Substitute some activity for emotional eating.
- ☐ Get enough sleep.
- ☐ Walk away from the food that is tempting you.
- ☐ Write down your feelings before you eat.
- ☐ Don't snack between meals.
- ☐ Stay away from sugar.
- ☐ Turn on some music and start dancing.
- ☐ Look at your food intake over a week instead of a day.
- ☐ Repeat affirmations daily.
- ☐ Crying can release stress. Allow yourself to cry.

© 2009 Rebecca Cooper   www.dietsdontwork.org   800-711-6336

Diet's Don't Work®

- ☐ Take a few deep breaths, close your eyes, and picture yourself in a peaceful place.
- ☐ Use positive language. For example, "I'm doing better this week than last week."
- ☐ Wait 15 minutes before you start to eat.
- ☐ Call someone.
- ☐ Have a cup of tea to signify the end of the meal.
- ☐ Plan a project immediately after eating a normal meal.
- ☐ Carry healthy snack foods with you for emergencies.
- ☐ Pack a healthy satisfying lunch to take to work.
- ☐ Quit talking about dieting with your friends at meals
- ☐ Remember how far you have come.
- ☐ Do something good for yourself:
- ☐ Write in a journal.
- ☐ Get out of your head.
- ☐ Plan some pleasure reading in the evenings.
- ☐ Take a walk.
- ☐ Do some drawing.
- ☐ Keep supportive loving people around you.
- ☐ Post affirmations to keep yourself on track.
- ☐ Go to a movie.
- ☐ Plan a vacation.
- ☐ Volunteer at a nursing home or animal shelter.
- ☐ Exercise at least three times a week if possible.
- ☐ Keep food locked up with a padlock.
- ☐ Pray.

© 2009 Rebecca Cooper   www.dietsdontwork.org   800-711-6336

CHAPTER 16 ***The Power of Purpose & Goals***

"There is no heavier burden than an unfulfilled potential."

Charles M. Schulz

In the Introduction, I wrote about how freeing myself from unhealthy eating patterns and the obsession with food enabled me to create a wonderful life. It made room for me to find my life's purpose – that is, helping others to free themselves from unproductive (and sometimes self-destructive) patterns around eating so they could eventually find their way to peace and purpose.

Among the greatest of life's pleasures is the possession of purpose to fill the days and goals to excite the mind.

What goals and purposes have you been missing out on in your life? Did your eating habits drain you of your energy? Could part of it be due to all the energy that the thoughts of food, diets, and body image consumed? This final chapter will help you begin to answer that question in the ultimate process of self-discovery.

Your Purpose Is Unique

You are the only person who can use your abilities.

Among the greatest of life's pleasures is the possession of purpose to fill the days and goals to excite the mind. The world is filled with people stuck with where they are, not knowing the joy of having a meaning and purpose in their life. To accept the challenge of your goal and believe in your purpose has a tendency to bring new excitement to life. At the close of the day, you can be proud of what you've done. You can look back on your life with a smile.

The frustration of potentiality is the root of neurosis.
- Ira Progoff, PhD.

We crave a higher purpose. Satisfying our ego wants alone does not bring real joy to our lives. Consequently, we may attain what we thought would bring us happiness only to find a feeling of being unsatisfied.

Perhaps you thought that when you finished school, or found the perfect mate, or had the right car or house, or had enough money, then you would be happy. In fact, you may even be thinking right now, *When I lose weight, then I will be happy.* Ironically, sometimes the most devastating place to be is to have it all, no longer having something to obtain to make our lives happy and still feel unfulfilled.

The other important piece of the puzzle is not in accumulating material possessions, but in attaining the joy inside that comes with a belief in living your life with meaning and purpose. This joy results when we align with our True Self and live our lives in conjunction with the inner promptings of our own uniqueness and passions in life.

Discovering Your Purpose

If we look at our passions in life, we will find clues to our meaning and purpose in life.

As we grow accustomed to being more internally directed, we naturally start to examine our lives.

If we look at our passions in life, we will find the first clue to our meaning and purpose. Consider, for instance, something you love doing. Within that, you will find keys to unlock your own unique purpose and meaning for this lifetime. What activity do you enjoy doing so much that you actually lose track of time? Following our passions opens us up enough to recognize the doors that will open for us when we are on this path. In time, this pursuit will reveal opportunities and more open doors. You will be led further down the path to your own purpose when you follow your passions.

Another point to recognize when identifying your purpose is this: *Don't be afraid to take risks.* Moving in new directions is risky, but necessary, in order to move ahead. We risk every day of our lives.

Risks must be taken because the greatest hazard in life is to risk nothing. The person who risks nothing, does nothing, and has nothing. They may avoid suffering and sorrow, but they cannot learn, feel, change, grow, or love. They have forfeited the freedom to be true to themselves. Only a person who risks is free to enjoy this adventure called life.

In light of all this we can see that we must discover our passions because they point us to our purpose in life. Once we recognize our passions, we can start establishing goals that will move us in that direction.

Finding Your Way

At first, it's not necessary to map out all of your goals at once. Just start investigating areas that encompass your passion and complete the small steps one at a time.

Don't be afraid to investigate new areas. Remember, you can always return to where you were. Bare in mind, it's only when we are so rigidly attached to our expectation of how the goal should be accomplished that we risk the chance of missing the possibilities. We need to be open and flexible for possible changes or problems that could be a blessing in disguise. It could put you on course to a life that is better than you ever dreamed or imagined.

It is helpful to exercise some basic practices to increase self-awareness. For example, take time for prayer and meditation. We can work ourselves into a whirlwind of unproductive activity if we fail to stay in touch with that peace within.

To laugh is to risk appearing foolish. To cry is to risk appearing weak. To reach out for another is to risk rejection. To expose feelings is to risk vulnerability. To love is to risk not being loved in return. To hope is to risk disappointment. To try is to risk failure. -William Arthur Ward

At first dreams seem impossible, then improbable, then inevitable. - Christopher Reeve

At this point, we are ready to set flexible goals or idea points. Remember, true success is the fulfillment of our life purpose or meaning; all other achievements feel empty and hollow without it.

The second step when setting a goal is to recognize the importance of making the goal measurable and realistic. Baby steps will get the ball rolling and it increases self-esteem as we go. This will keep us on track. Life is so busy, and it's so easy to get distracted if we don't have goals as our compass.

Although a goal gives us direction, it does not give us the necessary tools to get there. Discovering the proper tools is the next step. We form a plan of how to reach our goals, always being mindful of the synchronicity of events that propel us forward.

Opportunities will present themselves as you follow your passions.

Stay alert for new opportunities and direction in the disguise of problems. It's amazing how many times a problem can point us to a shortcut on our path. Meanwhile, if we don't have a goal set from our inner Self, we won't know which events to be mindful of. Our mind can become full of daily happenings, so we need to continue to take time to be still (meditate) to continue on our course.

> ## Failures... But Not Quite
>
> - After Fred Astaire's first screen test, a 1933 memo from the MGM testing director said, "Can't act. Slightly bald. Can dance a little." Astaire kept that memo over the fireplace in his Beverly Hill's home.
>
> - A relatively unsuccessful marketer of restaurant equipment, he didn't sell his first hamburger until age 52. At a time when many people prepare for retirement, Ray Kroc built McDonald's from a handful of hamburger stands into the world's largest fast food chain.
>
> - When his older brother was killed during WWII, he first withdrew into a shell. Then he began to listen to the radio to ease his pain. Soon he was dreaming about hosting his own radio show. That led Dick Clark to start American Bandstand.
>
> - Walt Disney was fired from a newspaper for lacking ideas. He also went bankrupt several times before he built Disneyland.

Figure 16.1: Failures?

Another important step consists of continually reminding yourself to be grateful for the successes along the way to your goal. Take time to acknowledge your successes. Share these successes with others. Success through perseverance helps to build self-esteem and confidence. Besides, your story may encourage someone else to move forward.

Take time to acknowledge your successes.

When you share your success with other people, this allows the flow of goodness to continue to impact others. It can give hope to someone else. This, in itself, can be a purpose and meaning in life. As it is given to you, give to others and watch the miracles multiply.

As it is given to you, give to others and watch the miracles multiply.

Job or Passion

Perhaps one of the most obvious places goals come into play is in our daily work. A popular myth worthy of investigation is that work has to be difficult. That is just not true. Our attitude toward work has been shaped by various teachings and perceptions. For instance, if we think we have to do a job by ourselves, we can feel overwhelmed. Yet, if we ask for help, we fear we will be thought less of.

Truthfully, what really makes work difficult is forgetting that God or our Higher Power is our spiritual partner. When our egos become attached to the work, we get in our own way of success. Once we get ourselves out of the way and ask for help, then God and others can help us.

Haven't you noticed the times in your life when you pushed and tugged at an idea, yet no matter how you tried to succeed, it failed? Compare that to the other times, when you knew what you were doing was right and everything just seemed to click into place. It seems that even though you worked for hours and returned home tired, you felt satisfied and whole, knowing that you had accomplished something beyond your ego. It felt sacred to your soul. In this type of instance, you cannot help but feel fulfilled and joyous. The effort becomes effortless and the challenges become adventures.

What really makes work difficult is forgetting that God or Higher Power who is our spiritual partner.

According to Jewish leader Rabbi Nachman of Breslov, "The fact that you may think you have to work hard for something diminishes your faith in God and in yourself. Your doubt shows you lack confidence in your partnership with God and in God's decision to choose you as a partner for the task. Although you may think you have faith in God, your faith is diminished when you do not have faith in yourself." Rabbi Nachman calls this *small thinking* and says that small thinking leads to small living.

Where Will You Spend Your Energy?

We need to Plan, Pursue, and Persevere.

We all have the same twenty-four hours in a day. The difference is how we spend our time and energy. Energy is meant to change form or be spent. What will you spend your precious life energy on after working your way through this book? Isn't it time to stop obsessing about weight, diet, food, or body image?

The choice is always ours, even if we feel we have no choice. Of course, it's hard to break out of our habitual patterns, but it can be done. We first need to see our habitual patterns in order to be aware of how we want to change. Look at each day. Start moving from where you are now. Visualize your goals.

Energy can be lost in procrastination, negative thinking, fear, food, or other obsessions. Mindless *zoning out* on food, TV, computer games, etc. all sap our precious energy. We do need to remember that we require down-time, but we also need to recognize how draining some of our downtime activities actually can be.

I would hate to be at the end of my life with no more time and realize I had postponed my life.

An Ongoing Story

Even after retirement or fulfilling our family life, we have much to give. As we age, we accumulate wisdom and experience that can make someone else's journey through life a little easier. Our golden years can provide a perspective for others, which could have been our purpose in life all along.

Always remember: There is no finish line. Life is made up of a process of accomplishing purposeful goals and dreams.

Isn't it time to stop obsessing about weight, diet, food, or body image?

Now the choice is yours…

…to leave the world a better place…to know one life has breathed easier because you have lived. This is to have succeeded.
- Ralph Waldo Emerson

CHAPTER EXERCISE: Part I. Finding Our Purpose

In questioning ourselves, we might ask:

- What made me happy as a kid?

- What did I dream of becoming when I was a child?

- What are my passions?

- What are my strengths?

- How can I use these strengths and passions?

© 2009 Rebecca Cooper   www.dietsdontwork.org   800-711-6336

Diets Don't Work®

Part II. Decide on 3 goals that are in alignment with Part I.

Goal	How will I know I have reached it?
1.	
2.	
3.	

Part III. Now list 3 steps to start each goal.

Goal 1.		
Goal 2.		
Goal 3.		

©2009 Rebecca Cooper

www.dietsdontwork.org

800-711-6336

Diets Don't Work®

Part IV. Overcoming Obstacles

Obstacles to Goals	Ways to Overcome Obstacles
Goal 1.	
Goal 2.	
Goal 3.	

© 2009 Rebecca Cooper

www.dietsdontwork.org

800-711-6336

Resources

American Dietetic Association
Nutrition hotline: (900) 225-5267
Publications: (800) 877-1600 ext. 5000
Web site: www.eatright.org
The American Dietetic Association operates a nutrition
hotline that provides the public with nutrition information
for a small fee. The association also offers publications
and other resources to the general public, health care
providers and other professionals, teachers, and parents.

Diets Don't Work® Structured Programs
Telephone: (800) 711-6336
Web site: www.DietsDontWork.org
E-mail: info@DietsDontWork.org
The Diets Don't Work® program was created to heal the
suffering caused by Compulsive Overeating, Binge Eating, Bulimia, Anorexia, and Food Addictions. The program of individual sessions provides a nurturing,
respectful, and safe environment that allows clients to
heal from the shame, guilt, and confusion associated with
these disorders. The clinicians' own experiences with
food addictions and eating disorders encourage openness,
hope, and healing. The program connects people back to
an internal form of control, making it possible to eat
when hungry, make healthy food choices, and stop eating
when full. Clients learn to identify the thoughts, feelings,
and situations that trigger using food or thinking exces-
sively about food, dieting, weight, and body image. The
Diets Don't Work® program is a structured program based
on cognitive-behavioral theory, solution-focused theory,
and educational awareness. It is complemented with
guided imagery, hypnotherapy, affirmations, and meditation techniques. It is complete with corresponding home-
work assignments, self-awareness assessments, progress

charts, and recorded guided imagery. In addition to the individual sessions, Diets Don't Work® also has Tele-groups, on-line sessions, and telephone sessions.

National Eating Disorders Association (NEDA)
Telephone: (206) 382-3587
Information and Referral Helpline:
(800) 931-2237
Web site: www.nationaleatingdisorders.org
NEDA is the largest eating disorders prevention and advocacy organization in the world. The association provides treatment referrals to those suffering from anorexia, bulimia, binge eating disorder, and to those concerned with body image and weight issues. NEDA also develops prevention programs for a wide range of audiences, publishes and distributes educational materials, conducts an annual conference, and operates a toll-free eating disorders helpline.

The National Heart, Lung, and Blood Institute (NHLBI)
Telephone: (301) 592-8573
Web site: www.nhlbi.nih.gov
E-mail: NHLBinfo@rover.nhlbi.nih.gov
The NHLBI Information Center and the Obesity Education Initiative provide information about weight control, including tools such as an online BMI calculator for adults and a menu planner. The NHLBI also operates a program called Hearts N' Parks, a partnership with the National Recreation and Parks Association, which helps provide activities for kids and adults that encourage healthy lifestyle choices to reduce the risk of obesity and heart disease.

National Institute of Diabetes and Digestive and Kidney Disease (NIDDK)
Telephone: (877) 946-4627
Web site: www.niddh.nih.gov

NIDDK offers statistics, research, and educational information on its Web site and manages The Weight-control Information Network (WIN), which provides resources on obesity, eating disorders and other weight-related issues.

The National Women's Health Information Center (NWHIC)
Telephone: (800) 994-9662
TDD: (888) 220-5446
Web site: www.4woman.gov
www.4girls.gov
NWHIC is a federal government Web site and toll-free call center that provides free, reliable women's health information. Sponsored by the Department of Health and Human Services' Office on Women's Health, NWHIC features special sections on body image and girls' health. The 4girls.gov Web site gives girls between the ages of 10 and 16 reliable, current health information designed to motivate them to choose healthy behaviors.

Rebecca's House Eating Disorder Treatment Programs™
Telephone: (800) 711-2062
Web site: www.RebeccasHouse.org
E-mail: intake@RebeccasHouse.org Rebecca's House Eating Disorders Treatment Programs™ provide several unique programs for people recovering from anorexia, bulimia, food addictions, yo-yo dieting, binge eating, obesity, and emotional overeating. Some of our clients are also challenged with drug abuse or alcoholism. The following types of programs are available:
Residential sober-living for Eating Disorders
Adult Women's Eating Disorder Outpatient Programs
Adolescent After-School Eating Disorder Program
Men's Eating Disorder Outpatient Program
Individual Counseling for Eating Disorders
Aftercare alumni and support groups
FREE Family Support Group for loved ones of those struggling with disordered eating.

List of Figures

Figure 2.1: The Conscious and Subconscious Mind

Figure 2.2: Food Coping Cycle

Figure 4.1: Words to Describe Feelings

Figure 4.2: Common Defenses

Figure 4.3: Understanding Our Feelings

Figure 4.4: Feeling Intensity Chart

Figure 5.1: Master of the Second Thought

Figure 5.2: Things to Think On

Figure 6.1: Limiting Beliefs

Figure 8.1: Journey to Self

Figure 14.1: Heal Your Feelings

Figure 14.2: Why Forgive?

Figure 16:1 Failures?

Index

Abandonment......................................*64*

Abuse...*63*

Acceptance..................................... 155

anger101, 122, 138, 149, 152, 153, 154, 155, 156, 174, 176, 181, 182, 186

Anger ...*68, 71, 152, 153, 160, 182, 187*

Anxiety *75, 149, 150, 151*

anxious..26, 31, 35, 37, 41, 43, 56, 139, 149, 150, 151, 173

appetite.... ix, 20, 21, 24, 33, 38, 53, 55, 194, 196, 223

Assertion... 174

Assertiveness *171, 172*

assessment ....ix, 28

awareness iii, viii, ix, 20, 22, 28, 33, 39, 49, 53, 62, 65, 80, 89, 93, 151, 166, 177, 182, 185, 187, 188, 203, 215

balance....22, 36, 52, 53, 106, 138, 155, 172

beliefs....36, 51, 88, 89, 91, 94, 97, 106, 122, 123, 125, 127, 138, 150, 157

Beliefs............................ *87, 88, 90, 91*

Binge Eating *215*

Boredom *160*

Boundaries *101, 102, 103, 104, 105, 106, 110*

breakfast..24

Charlie Finn 47

checklists..ix

Control *18, 62, 78, 138, 148*

Dependence............................. *164, 167*

depressed.... 26, 35, 41, 49, 52, 56, 115, 139, 182, 195, 196

Eleanor Roosevelt 59

Emotional Eating *34, 135, 143, 184*

Emptiness..*163*

Exercise................................*25, 49, 89*

fat-free 25

Fear *68, 75, 118, 154, 155, 160*

Food Coping Cycle *36, 37*

forgiveness...................... 165, 182, 189

Forgiveness.............................. *181, 182*

form ..... i, ix, 20, 37, 51, 52, 77, 87, 93, 185, 204, 206, 215 forms .... ix, 28, 62, 77, 124, 127

Freedom .... ii, 38, 64, 65, 96

gastric bypass surgery 18

Goals *201, 213*

God ...45, 50, 91, 92, 93, 107, 108, 109, 117, 118, 140, 159, 164, 165, 166, 167, 206, 224

Grief *68, 156*

guided imageries ix

happiness ..65, 114, 116, 149, 157, 158, 202

Higher Power ... 50, 65, 91, 92, 93, 107, 118, 140, 164, 165, 166, 206

hurt 32, 63, 64, 103, 107, 110, 114, 149, 152, 153, 154, 155, 172, 182, 183

Isolation *23*

Journaling . *75, 113, 114, 115, 116, 120, 165*

Kirlian photography 52

Loneliness *156, 160*

lonely 22, 23, 43, 45, 156, 163

love . viii, 22, 27, 28, 32, 46, 64, 79, 94, 107, 116, 118, 119, 124, 125, 129, 130, 149, 188, 189, 202, 203, 217

low-fat 17, 24, 25

Mahatma Gandhi 88

manipulating 63

Marcus Aurelius 73

Meditation *143, 166*

metabolism 21, 24, 25, 194, 197

mistakes ... 78, 121, 128, 130, 141, 156, 158, 165, 174

negative thoughts 91, 93, 128, 141, 150, 152

peace ...53, 95, 116, 149, 155, 158, 165, 166, 168, 184, 187, 201, 203

procrastinate 33

purpose ...... viii, 79, 114, 158, 164, 168, 176, 202

Rabbi Harold Kushner 54

reaction .. 59, 66, 67, 68, 101, 115, 179, 182, 185, 186

relationships ..... vii, 27, 28, 44, 73, 115, 122, 124, 130, 148, 152, 153, 163, 175, 223

resentments 182, 183, 189

responsibility 22, 33, 79, 105, 129, 130, 136, 139, 173, 175, 176

Self-Esteem *121, 123, 127, 130, 131, 156*

Self-Forgiveness 188, 189, 190

self-talk .38, 39, 43, 74, 75, 77, 81, 117, 127

spirituality 23, 45, 48, 92, 93, 107, 149, 157, 164, 165, 166, 167, 169

Spirituality .. *50, 96, 140, 164, 167, 169*

stress 33

subconscious.... 27, 80, 81, 88, 89, 123, 125, 127, 128, 130, 187

sugar ...v, 32, 49, 54, 56, 196, 197, 198, 223

T.S. Eliot... 43

telephone sessions............................. 49

True Self . 22, 27, 44, 62, 123, 149, 202

values....88, 89, 91, 94, 95, 96, 97, 106, 157, 158

Values *94, 222*

William Faulkner 87

About the Author

When Rebecca was four years old, her father was killed. A year later, her mother left her and her sister with a babysitter and never came back! She lived in foster care and then with her aging grandparents. Her grandfather died while she was in sixth grade. The unresolved grief caused her to find a way to numb the feelings.

Her first drug of choice was sugar. She would eat candy or think about her weight, diet, food, and body image as a diversion. Food became a coping mechanism. She would overeat and then restrict food. This put her on a roller coaster of diets and binges that sent her into the vortex of an eating disorder that consumed twenty years of her life. Rebecca was eating and restricting food, which is commonly identified as compulsive overeating or binge eating, bulimia, and anorexia.

Her grandmother died on her sixteenth birthday, leaving her and her sister homeless. She lived with neighbors, distant relatives, and finally her favorite high school teacher, Ernie Capehart and her family, until she went to college. Rebecca was working her way through college dealing with the financial, academic, and emotional stress with food.

She found drugs to control her overwhelming appetite and cravings. She started adding alcohol to her addictions and finally hit her bottom on February 25, 1986. Rebecca has been clean and sober since then.

Her first year of recovery was so precarious because of the eating disorder. After almost a year of sobriety, Rebecca was freed from the merry go round of yo-yo dieting and eating disorders.

Rebecca's low self-esteem attracted her to abusive relationships. During that marriage, she wanted love so badly that she thought to have a baby would make the happy family that she had always wanted. She stayed clean and sober through six miscarriages. Along with her 12-Step work, she did the recovery work of *coming home to her Self.* This process allowed her to enter into a loving, nurturing marriage.

Today, she finds her experience invaluable as she helps people change their eating habits and abstain from other addictive behaviors. She obtained her Masters in Clinical Psychology at Pepperdine University. She is a licensed therapist, Certified Eating Disorder Specialist (CEDS), She is the author of the Diet's Don't Work® Structured Program. This program is used by therapists, counselors, dietitians, treatment centers, and recovery homes. She is the founder of Rebecca's House, an extended care residence for eating disorders in Southern California, and Rebecca's House Eating Disorder Treatment Programs™.

Rebecca's mother died a few years ago. The doctor used the term "morbid obesity" with regard to her mother's demise. Her mother still didn't believe she had a problem with food. When Rebecca went back to her home in Ohio, she found half-eaten boxes of cookies and gallons of ice cream. Right up to the day she went to the hospital, Rebecca's mother was trying to comfort herself the best way she knew how—with food. Rebecca became even more devoted to her cause.

"I've always believed that good comes out of bad. However, I never felt that belief applied to the suffering I experienced as a result of my addictions. But today, when I see a young woman recovering from the same disease that plagued me for so long, I realize that God had a plan bigger than I could have ever imagined."

Ordering Information

--The Structured Program

Books are available at a quantity discount for recovery centers, treatment centers, and schools.

To purchase books or to get more information, go to www.DietsDontWork.org or call 800-711-6336.